READ WELL

From Generation to Generation

UNITS 8, 9

ISBN 978-1-60218-552-4
ISBN 1-60218-552-2
167265

12 11 10 09 08   2 3 4 5 6

Sopris West®
EDUCATIONAL SERVICES

A Cambium Learning Company

BOSTON, MA · LONGMONT, CO

UNIT 8 • Traditional Tales

UNIT 9 • Family Tales

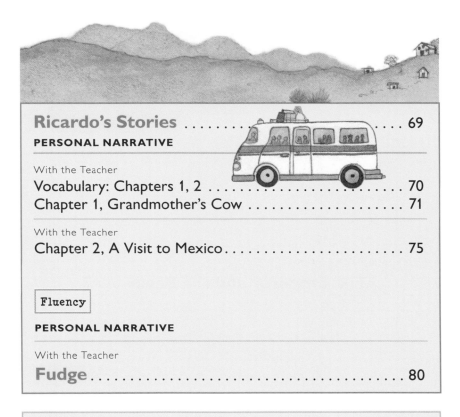

UNIT 8
Traditional Tales

The Emperor and the Seed

a folktale from ancient China
retold by Marilyn Sprick
illustrated by Robert McGuire

Look at the picture. Where and when do you think the story takes place?
What do you think you will learn?

Chapters 1, 2

Vocabulary

★ an·cient

Ancient means very, very old. Something that is ancient may be thousands of years old.

The *ancient* buildings were falling down. Look at the picture. What tells you that the buildings may be ancient?

★ em·per·or

An **emperor** is the leader of a country or countries.

What does an *emperor* do? What is the leader in the picture called?

★ suc·ces·sor

A **successor** is the person who takes over someone's job.

Bill retired as the coach of the baseball team. The new coach is Grace. Grace is Bill's . . .

★ = New

★ wealth·y

Wealthy means to have a lot of something—usually money.

A *wealthy* person is someone who has a lot of money. The emperor was . . .

★ dis·ap·point·ed

Disappointed means to have a feeling of sadness when you don't get what you want.

When they couldn't go on the field trip, the children were sad. What's another way to say "The children were sad because they didn't get what they wanted"? The children were . . .

★ sum·mon

Summon means to order someone to come to a place.

What's another way to say "The Emperor ordered the people to the palace"? The Emperor . . .

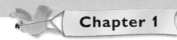

Chapter 1

The Emperor

In ancient times, there was a wise and beloved emperor. He ruled the land with fairness and kindness. With no children of his own, the Emperor needed to choose his successor.

Word spread rapidly across the empire. Wealthy parents brought their children from all over the land. Each mother was certain her child would be chosen.

What was the Emperor's goal? Why do you think he was trying to find a *successor*?

Hundreds of children, dressed in the finest hand-painted silk, were brought to the Emperor. A line of boys stretched around the palace wall. The Emperor thought for sure he would know when he met the right child.

Day after day, the Emperor thought, "Today is the day. Today is the day that I will meet the next emperor!" But every day he was disappointed.

Why was the Emperor *disappointed?*

The Emperor walked in the quiet of his garden. He thought to himself, "The boys wear the finest silks. They are from the best of families. They all show me the greatest respect, but they all seem the same. What shall I do?"

The Emperor could hear the hum of the bees. The graceful plum blossoms fluttered in the gentle wind. They almost seemed to whisper. Finally, in the peace of his garden, the Emperor knew what he would do.

MAIN CHARACTER

1. Who is the main character?

CHARACTERIZATION

2. Describe the Emperor.

GOAL, INFERENCE

3. What is the Emperor's goal? Why?

INFERENCE

4. What kind of person do you think the Emperor wants for his successor?

Chapter 2

The Seed

Again, the children were summoned to the palace. A long line of boys formed around the palace wall. One by one, the boys entered the palace. One by one, the boys in their fine silks were given a small seed. Each boy was told to plant the seed and bring it back in the spring. Each boy placed his seed in a small silk bag.

What do you think the Emperor wants the boys to do? How do you think he will choose the next emperor?

Finally, all the young boys had taken their seeds home. One seed remained. The Emperor returned to his garden. There, an old gardener and his grandson were pruning the plum tree. The grandfather held his grandson's hand and showed him how to make the cuts. Snip. Snip. The little boy's dark eyes danced with happiness.

Why do you think the boy was happy?

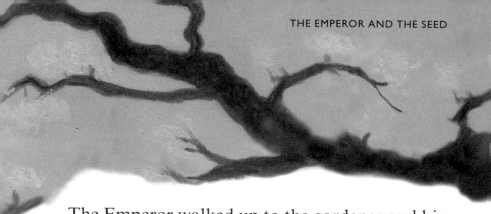

The Emperor walked up to the gardener and his grandson. "Show me what you are doing," said the Emperor. Then the Emperor, the gardener, and the little boy watered, weeded, and pruned until the sky grew dark.

As the gardener packed his tools, the Emperor held out his hand to the little boy. "Take this seed," he said. "Plant it and then bring it back to me in the spring." The little boy's eyes grew large with wonder. He placed the lovely little seed in a small cloth bag. Then he carefully wrapped the package with string and tied it with a knot—just to be sure the seed would be safe.

As the boy and his grandfather left the garden, the Emperor said, "What is your name?"

The small boy said, "My name is Jun (Jen)."

What do you think the boy will do with the seed? How can you tell the boy will take good care of his seed? What is Jun's goal?

Chapter 3

Vocabulary

★ ad·vice

Advice is what someone tells others they should do.

Sometimes I have trouble getting up in the morning. Do you have any *advice* for me?

★ brag

Brag means to talk proudly about things you own or things you've done.

Tom *bragged* about how strong he was. What do you think Tom might have said?

★ em·bar·rassed

Embarrassed means to be uncomfortable or nervous and worried about something you've said or done.

When Tim dropped his lunch, he was . . .

★ = New

★ de·spite

Despite is another way to say "even though."

"*Despite* eating a big lunch, I was still hungry" is another way to say "Even though I ate a big lunch, I was still hungry."

What's another way to say "Even though I took a nap, I am still tired"? Start with "Despite taking . . ."

★ in·teg·ri·ty

Integrity is complete honesty. A person who has integrity always tells the truth and does the right thing.

Maria showed *integrity* when she told her mom that she broke the window. How did Maria show integrity? What are ways that you show integrity?

Now You Try It!

Try defining each word. Then look up the word in the glossary. Your definition might be better!

an·cient

Start with "*Ancient* means . . ."
Let's find the word on page 82.

suc·ces·sor

Start with "A *successor* is the person who . . ."
Let's find the word on page 86.

Chapter 3

The Successor

Across the land, children planted their seeds in beautiful bowls. Jun planted his seed in an ordinary clay pot. Then the boy took care of the seed—just as his grandfather had taught him.

He gave the seed fish food. He watered, and he weeded, and he left the pot in the warm spring sun. To his great surprise, nothing happened.

Jun asked his grandfather for advice. His grandfather said, "Be patient. Some plants need time."

When spring came, children across the land could be seen with big plants in their pots. Each child bragged, "Mine is best. The Emperor will choose me."

Jun was embarrassed. Nothing grew in his pot. Still, he watered, and he weeded, and he made sure that sunlight warmed the pot.

Finally, the children were asked to bring their plants to the palace. Jun did not want to go. His grandfather said, "You must go, Jun. When it is your turn, tell the Emperor that you have done your best."

Who is this part of the story about? What is Jun's problem? Why is Jun *embarrassed*? What was his grandfather's *advice*?

Jun stood in line at the palace wall. The other children made fun of his plain clothes and empty pot. The little boy's dark eyes grew darker, but he did not say a word.

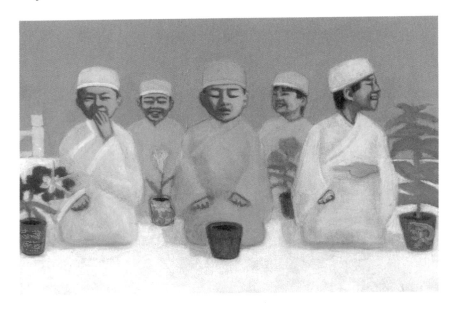

Finally, the Emperor invited all the children into the palace. The Emperor gazed at the fancy bowls, the huge plants, and the colorful blossoms. "Ah, they are quite beautiful," said the Emperor.

Then, to everyone's surprise, the Emperor asked Jun and his grandfather to come sit near him. A hush fell over the room.

A hush fell over the room. What do you think that means? Why do you think that happened?

The Emperor said, "The gardener has raised his grandson well. Like each of you, Jun was given one seed. He watered the seed and weeded around it. He made sure the sun warmed the seed. Despite his care, nothing grew. I cooked all of your seeds, so they could not grow. When Jun's seed did not grow, he did not lie. He was honest and brought me his empty pot."

"Jun will grow into a man of great integrity," the Emperor said. "He will treat you with fairness and honesty. One day, Jun will be Emperor of all China."

Why did the other boys disappoint the Emperor? How did Jun show that he had *integrity*? Why did the Emperor choose Jun to be his successor?

Story Retell

The Emperor and the Seed
Character Comparison

Setting (When/Where): In ancient times, in China		
Main Characters		
Goals	Emperor's Goal: To find a successor	Jun's Goal:
Problem	Emperor's Problem: First, the Emperor couldn't find a successor.	Jun's Problem:
Action	Emperor's Action: Next, the Emperor gave seeds to the boys. He gave Jun the last seed. In the spring, the Emperor summoned the boys back.	Jun's Action:
Outcome/ Conclusion	The Emperor chose Jun to be his successor because Jun had integrity.	
Lesson	Be honest and you will be rewarded.	

Stone Soup

a folktale from England
retold by Karen Akiyama-Paik and Marilyn Sprick
illustrated by Eugenia Nobati

Acts 1, 2

Vocabulary

★ **folk·tale**

A **folktale** is a story that people tell each other and pass along from one generation to the next.

The "Emperor and the Seed" is a *folktale*. What country is it from?

★ **vil·lage**

A **village** is like a town, but smaller. A village is a place where people live and work.

The people from the small mountain *village* came into town to buy things. What's a very small town called?

★ **min·strel**

A **minstrel** is a person who lived long ago and traveled from place to place singing and playing music.

If you lived in a village long ago, what would you think if *minstrels* came to your town?

con·tent·ed

Contented means happy and satisfied with something.

What does *contented* mean? Complete this sentence: After eating the luscious soup, the man was . . .

When do you feel contented?

★ = New

★ scarce

When something is **scarce**, there is not enough for everyone.

During the winter, food is *scarce* for the forest animals. Complete this sentence: Snow was on the ground so food was . . .

★ ap·pre·ci·ate

Appreciate means to be thankful for something.

We *appreciate* the teachers because they help us learn new things.

Who do you appreciate? Why?

★ cu·ri·ous

Someone who is **curious** wants to know more about something.

Sandy wanted to learn more about plants. She was . . .

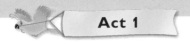

Act 1

A Meal for a Song

Setting:

A village in England long ago

Characters:

Narrator 1	Young Boy
Narrator 2	Cedric
Narrator 3	Ann
Narrator 4	Phillip
Old Man	All
Young Girl	

All: A merry band of minstrels strolled along a forest path. They talked happily and played sweet music. Ann played her recorder, Cedric strummed his lute, and Phillip told stories through songs.

Narrator 1: The minstrels were contented with what little they had. They earned their meals by singing. People often gave them bowls of homemade stew or freshly baked muffins.

Look at the picture. How did the *minstrels* get their food? Why were they *contented*?

Narrator 2: As they walked out of the forest, the minstrels noticed a small village. They hoped to find something to eat and a place to sleep.

Narrator 3: The village was poor. Life had been hard for many years. Food was scarce, and the people did not trust outsiders. There was little happiness.

Narrator 4: When the villagers saw the minstrels coming, they closed their windows tight.

All: The children hid. The minstrels sensed eyes staring at them through the cracks around the doors. They could hear whispering.

Describe life in the *village*. Why did the villagers hide from the minstrels?

All: The minstrels stopped in the middle of the village square. They walked up to a sad-looking old man sitting under a tree.

Cedric: Kind sir, we have traveled far and would appreciate a bite of food.

Old Man: We have too little food to even feed ourselves.

Narrator 1: Ann and Cedric took out their instruments. Slowly, sweet music started to drift through the village. Curious villagers began to poke their heads out of doors.

Phillip: The villagers are sad. We will bring happiness to this place.

Why wouldn't the villagers share food with the minstrels? What did the minstrels want to bring to the villagers? How could they make the villagers happy?

Narrator 2: Children inched their way closer and closer. A few people gathered and began to hum along with the minstrels.

Ann: The villagers are hungry. Let's bring full stomachs to this village.

Phillip: Cedric, I think it is time for us to make some of your scrumptious stone soup.

Young Girl: Scrumptious. What's that?

Cedric: Scrumptious means delicious. We're going to make a delicious stone soup.

Young Boy: Stone soup. What's that?

Cedric: Ah, stone soup is wonderful for hungry minstrels and their friends.

All: The minstrels had quite a job to do. The village was poor, and the people seemed to have no food. Still, the minstrels were set on making a scrumptious meal for themselves and the villagers.

Reread Narrator 2's part at the top of the page. What do you think is happening to a few of the villagers?

Think and Talk

CHARACTERS

1. Who is the play about?

SETTING

2. Where does the play take place?

CHARACTERIZATION

3. Describe the villagers.

INFERENCE

4. Why are the villagers unhappy?

GOAL

5. What did the minstrels want to do?

PREDICTION

6. What do you think will happen next?

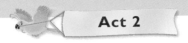

Act 2

A Pot of Water and Three Small Stones

Setting:

The village square

Characters:

Narrator 1	Young Boy
Narrator 2	Cedric
Narrator 3	Ann
Narrator 4	Phillip
Old Woman	All
Young Girl	

All: Three hungry minstrels had strolled into a village where the people were poor and unhappy. The minstrels were determined to make a scrumptious meal.

Narrator 3: Hearing talk about food, people around the village cracked open their doors. Slowly, people came out of their homes. The minstrels stood in the center of the square.

Describe the villagers. What made them begin to come out of their homes?

Ann: We need a fire to make our luscious soup.

Young Girl: Luscious? What's that?

Ann: Luscious means wonderful and delicious. We're going to make a luscious stone soup.

Narrator 4: Ann began gathering sticks, then started a small fire. The young boy and girl helped gather more wood. Others began to help. In no time, a hot fire crackled in the square.

Narrator 1: Phillip pulled out a small pot and three round stones from his pack.

Cedric: We'll need some water.

Young Girl: I'll get some.

Narrator 2: Cedric dropped three stones into the small pot of water. Soon it was steaming.

Do you think the minstrels can make a luscious pot of soup with three stones and water? What would make their soup luscious?

Phillip: It's too bad our pot is so small. If we had a bigger pot, we could make enough soup to share with everyone.

Old Woman: I will let you use my pot.

Phillip: Thank you, kind lady. We will be certain to give you some stone soup.

Narrator 3: Soon the stones were boiling in a bigger pot. More and more villagers gathered to see what the commotion was about. Cedric tasted the soup.

Cedric: Mmm. This broth would be so much better with a bit of salt. But I shouldn't wish for what I can't have.

Young Boy: I can get some salt from my mother.

Phillip: Ah, this stone soup will be very good. But wouldn't some onions make it even more scrumptious?

Who loaned the minstrels a bigger pot? Who will bring salt to the minstrels?

Cedric: Yes, onions would make this the most delicious soup we've ever had. But I should not wish for something I can't have.

Young Girl: My mother says we can spare some onions.

Ann: Oh, kind young girl, we hope you and your mother will have soup with us.

Young Girl: And father too? He is sick in bed.

Ann: Of course! Stone soup is the best medicine for everybody!

All: The village was no longer quiet. More and more people gathered in the square to see what was happening. A pot of salted water sat on a hot fire.

Who will bring onions to the minstrels? Why is the village square no longer quiet?

Think and Talk

ACTION

1. What are the minstrels doing?

GOALS

2. What are the minstrels' goals?

CHARACTERIZATION

3. Describe how the villagers are starting to change.

Act 3

Vocabulary

★ i·ma·gine

Imagine means to make a picture of something in your mind. You can also imagine how something might smell, taste, and feel.

Imagine flying like a bird. What would it feel like?

* lus·cious

Luscious means delicious and mouth-watering. Something that is luscious has a delicious taste or smell.

The ripe peach was . . . *luscious*. Describe a food that you think tastes or smells luscious.

*This word was first defined in the context of the story.

★ = New

con·tent·ed

Contented means happy and satisfied with something.

The minstrels were *contented* with their lives. How did they feel?

★ mer·ry

Merry means happy and cheerful.

As the boy skipped down the path, he whistled a *merry* tune.

Was the tune sad or happy?

Now You Try It!

Try defining each word. Then look up the word in the glossary. Your definition might be better!

* scrump·tious

Start with "*Scrumptious* means . . ." Let's find the word on page 86.

★ won·der·ful

Start with "*Wonderful* is another word for . . ." Let's find the word on page 87.

*This word was first defined in the context of the story.

★ = New

Act 3

A Luscious Pot of Soup

Setting:

The village square

Characters:

Narrator 1	Young Boy
Narrator 2	Cedric
Narrator 3	Ann
Narrator 4	Phillip
Old Man	All

All: In a poor village, three hungry minstrels stood in the square making stone soup. The thin soup had only water and a bit of salt.

Narrator 4: A young girl brought her mother and sick father to the village square. Just as she had promised, the girl had a bowl of chopped onions for the soup. She poured the onions into the pot.

Phillip: Hmmm . . . what a wonderful smell. This stone soup will be very good. Imagine if we had a carrot or two to sweeten it up. But I shouldn't wish for what I can't have.

Old Man: A carrot? For a taste of the soup, I may be able to find a carrot to add to the soup.

Cedric: Bring a bunch of carrots and some celery and you shall have a whole bowl of scrumptious soup!

Narrator 1: The old man hurried away and was soon back with carrots and celery.

How are the villagers making the soup better? Some villagers have shared things for the soup. How do you think those villagers feel?

Phillip: Ah, what a wonderful smell. This will be a very, very good soup.

Cedric: Ann, what was it that made our last stone soup so very, very scrumptious?

Ann: Sweet red potatoes!

Phillip: Ah, sweet red potatoes. That is right. But I shouldn't wish for what I can't have.

Young Boy: My father has a few potatoes that we can put in the soup.

Ann: This stone soup will be just as good as the last pot!

All: One by one, people began to bring something for the soup. For the first time in years, the village square buzzed with excitement. The air was filled with wonderful smells. Finally, the big pot of soup was ready!

The story says, "The village square buzzed with excitement." What do you think that means? Why do you think the villagers were excited?

Narrator 2: Villagers brought tables, bowls, spoons, rice, bread, and sweet cakes. They all ate until they were content. After the scrumptious, luscious, oh-so-wonderful meal, the people sang, danced, and told stories of better times.

Narrator 3: Old friends laughed, hugged, and wondered what had happened to the good times. The three minstrels stood watching with contented stomachs and merry eyes.

Close your eyes. *Imagine* the village square. What do you hear? See? Smell?

Cedric: We have brought togetherness back to the village.

Phillip: We have brought sharing back to the village.

Ann: We have brought happiness back to the village.

All: Sounds of joy drifted in the air as Cedric, Phillip, and Ann departed. Music and song went with them, but it also remained in the village. Happiness was found in the simple making of stone soup.

Why were the villagers contented? What did the minstrels bring to the village? How was happiness found in the making of stone soup?

Story Comparison

Traditional Tales

Story	Stone Soup	The Emperor and the Seed
Setting: Where and when	England, long ago	
Goal	Minstrels' goal: To get a good meal Minstrels' goal for the villagers:	Emperor's goal: Jun's goal:
Action	Minstrels' action: Made stone soup Villagers' action:	Emperor's action: Jun's action:
Conclusion	The villagers helped make stone soup and discovered happiness.	
Lesson	Sharing and community bring happiness.	

UNIT 9
Family Tales

Judith and Ricardo both grew up in California. They worked hard in school, went to college, and earned their doctorates in school psychology.

Judith's Story

a personal narrative
by Judith Plasencia-Peinado, Ph.D.
illustrated by Johanna Van Der Sterre

From *generation* to generation, families grow, move, and experience new things. Every family has its own stories, and every story is special.

In this unit, you will meet Judith and Ricardo. They are real people with their own special stories. We are happy that they have shared their stories with us. After you finish reading this unit, we hope you will share your own stories with your classmates.

Chapters 1, 2

Vocabulary

★ im·mi·grate

Immigrate means to move to another country.

Maya's father moved to the United States from Costa Rica. Complete this sentence: Maya's father . . .

★ per·mis·sion

Permission is being told that you can do something.

You should always ask your parents for their *permission* to visit a friend.

To bring a pet to school, you need the teacher's . . .

★ = New

gen·er·a·tion

Within a family, there are grandparents, parents, and children. Each group is called a **generation**.

Your grandparents and their brothers and sisters are one *generation*. Your parents, aunts, and uncles are another . . .

You, your brothers, sisters, and cousins are yet another generation. The chart shows three generations of a family.

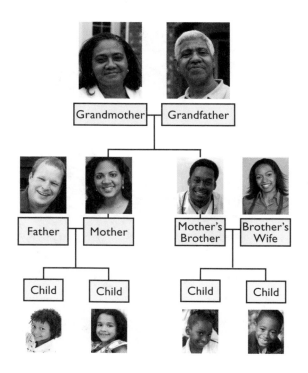

Chapter 1

Immigrating to the United States

Hello. My name is Judith. My husband, Ricardo, and I have two children. Their names are Isabel and Daniel. They like me to tell them about immigrating to the United States. Isabel says, "Mami, tell me about when you were seven. Tell me how you came to the United States from Mexico." Isabel often says this when it is time to go to bed!

Who is telling the story?

I say to Isabel, "You already know this story, and it is time to go to bed."

Isabel says, "Yes, but tell me again."

I look at the clock and say, "Okay. We have just enough time."

Isabel smiles, and I begin. "Do you remember how old I was?"

Isabel says, "Yes, Mami. You were seven."

Why do you think Isabel asked to hear her mother's story again?

"That's right. I was seven when we came from Mexico. We waited a long time to come to this country. It took many years for your grandmother and grandfather to get permission to come to the United States."

Judith and her family immigrated to the
United States nearly 40 years ago.

Isabel asks, "Why did Abuela (Ah-bway-lah) and Abuelo (Ah-bway-loh) have to get permission to come here?"

How old was Judith when she moved to the United States? How long ago was that?

Isabel asks many questions. Soon she will be able to tell my story. Daniel is still very little. He doesn't ask questions, but he listens very carefully.

I explain, "Abuelo and Abuela were born in Mexico. They wanted to work in the United States, so they needed to get permission from this country to come and work."

Think and Talk

NARRATOR
1. Who is telling this story? What do you know about her?

INFERENCE
2. It sounds like Isabel and Daniel have a bedtime tradition. What do you think it might be?

INFERENCE
3. Why do you think Judith is happy to tell her story over and over again?

EXPLANATION
4. Why did Judith's family want to immigrate, or move, to the United States?

Chapter 2

The Tall Buildings

Isabel knows what will come next in my story. She says, "Mami, were you surprised to see tall buildings?"

I say, "Yes, I was surprised, Isabel. Mexico has many big cities, but I had never been to them. I lived in a small village. The tallest building in the village was our church. It had one floor and a very tall roof, but it was not tall like a city building."

I tell the children, "Our journey from Mexico was very long. We were crammed into a bus with all our belongings. We kept falling asleep."

I ask Daniel, "How long was our ride?"

He says, "Loooooonnnng." Daniel is very proud of himself because he can help me tell my story too.

"I remember waking up. I looked out the window and could not believe my eyes. I shook my mami. 'Mami, wake up. What is that?' I asked.

"My mami looked out the window and said sleepily, 'What do you mean, Judith?' I remember looking up at the tall buildings. Mami said, 'Oh, those are buildings, Judith.'"

How did Judith and her family get to the United States? What surprised Judith? Why were the tall buildings a surprise? What's the tallest building you've ever seen?

57

"'Buildings? Why are they so big?' I asked.

"Mami said, 'Hundreds of people work in the buildings, so they must be big.' I sat quietly thinking about that. The buildings were so tall they looked like they touched the sun.

"Finally, I asked, 'How do people get to the top of the buildings?'

"Mami smiled. 'Ah, they have elevators.'

"I asked, 'What's an elevator?'

"My mother said, 'An elevator is a big box that people get into. It goes up and down. People push buttons so they can get on and off when they want.'

"I asked, 'Can I ride on an elevator?'

"My mother said, 'I will take you and your brother to a tall building, and we will ride in the elevator.'

"I couldn't wait."

When I finish my elevator story, Isabel and Daniel know that it is really time to get ready for bed!

When Judith arrived in the United States, what did she see that was very different from Mexico? What questions did she ask her mother?

Chapters 3, 4

Vocabulary

im·mi·grate

Immigrate means to move to another country.

Complete this sentence: In this story, Judith and her family . . .

gen·er·a·tion

Within a family, there are grandparents, parents, and children. Each group is called a **generation**.

This is a family tree. What does it show?

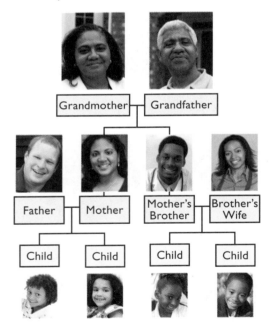

★ = New

Chapter 3

Going to School in America

Sometimes before bedtime, I tell Isabel and Daniel about first going to school in the United States. I say, "Oh my. The first day Mami took me to school, I remember looking in the classroom. It seemed like everyone had blond hair and blue eyes— even the teacher!"

I tell Isabel and Daniel, "It surprised me to see so many people with blond hair and light skin because everyone in Mexico had dark hair and brown eyes. I was a little scared. I looked different, and I did not speak English."

Why did Judith feel funny her first day of school? If she came to our school, would she feel differently? What would we do to make her feel welcome?

Isabel thinks this is funny because her school has many children with dark hair and dark skin and many children with blond hair and light skin too.

"Every day, I went to another room to learn English. My teacher was very nice. She gave candy to us when we worked hard."

Daniel, Isabel, and I always laugh together when I tell this part of my story. Isabel says, "No one ever gives us candy at school!"

I say to Isabel, "This was long ago! After all, I am ancient!"

After we laugh, I tell the children a little more about my education. "In my school, I did learn to speak English, and I made many friends.

"I also learned about a tradition in the United States. I learned about Thanksgiving, and when I was seven, I was thankful for my school. I was thankful to have new friends, and I was thankful that my family immigrated to the United States. I am still thankful for all of those things!"

Think and Talk

EXPLANATION

1. How did Judith feel about her first day of school?

MAKING CONNECTIONS

2. What do we do in our school to help new students feel welcome?

COMPARE/CONTRAST

3. How is your school the same or different from the school Judith went to?

INFERENCE

4. How do you know Judith was glad that she had immigrated to the United States?

Chapter 4

Lovely Green Lawns

One night, I say to the children, "I think you are ready to hear about the lovely green lawns."

The children look at me. "Lawns?" asks Isabel. "Is it a funny story?"

I say, "Yes, it is funny, because the one thing I remember the most about coming to the United States is the lawns."

Isabel says, "I think that is a very funny thing to remember."

I explain, "Where I lived in Mexico, the houses were very small and there were no yards. The houses had dirt and sometimes tile around them. My small country village was so different. Before I came to the United States, I had never seen a lawn. Imagine that!"

Isabel giggles, so Daniel giggles too. I say, "A lawn is a beautiful thing!"

Why did Judith think a lawn was so beautiful?

I say to the children, "Oh my, this story is funnier than I thought it would be."

I ask, "Do you know what my dream was?"

Isabel says, "A million dollars?"

I say, "Oh no. When I came to the United States, my dream was to have a nice house, a lovely green lawn, and a good education. This was my dream."

When I say this, Isabel and Daniel smile. I wonder if they are too young to understand, but Isabel says, "I have a nice house."

Then Daniel says, "Me too."

Then Isabel says, "We have a green lawn too, but we have to mow the lawn."

At that, Ricardo laughs. We all laugh!

We hug the kids and put them to bed. Someday I will tell the children how Ricardo and I got our house and green lawn.

But for now, I will tell you. My mami and papi said I should work hard in school. That is what I did. That is what Ricardo did too. We got a very good education and good jobs. We help teachers work with children who are immigrants. We also have a wonderful family. I have much to be thankful for!

Why do you think Judith feels so lucky?

Story Retell

JUDITH'S STORY

We're going to retell Judith's story.

Who is the narrator?

● At the beginning of the story,
what did you learn about Judith?
Use the word *immigrated*.

■ What happened in the middle
of the story after Judith and her
family arrived in the United States?

▲ What did you learn at
the end of Judith's story?

Ricardo's Stories

a personal narrative
by Ricardo Peinado, Ph.D.
illustrated by Johanna Van Der Sterre

From generation to generation, families grow and experience new things. Every family and every family member has his or her own stories to tell. These are a few of Ricardo's own stories. He is happy to share his stories with you.

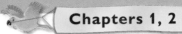

Chapters 1, 2

Vocabulary

gen·er·a·tion

Within a family, there are grandparents, parents, and children. Each group is called a **generation**.

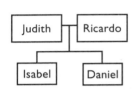

Judith — Ricardo
Isabel — Daniel

Judith and Ricardo are one *generation*. Who is in the next generation of Judith and Ricardo's family?

per·mis·sion

Permission is being told that you can do something.

Judith's parents were told they could live and work in the United States. They were given . . .

★ glis·ten

Glisten means to sparkle or look shiny.

A pool of water *glistens* in the sun. Use the word *glisten* to describe how a diamond looks in the sunlight.

★ drows·y

When you are drowsy, you are very sleepy.

If you are *drowsy*, you might want to take a nap. If you go to bed late at night, the next day you may be . . .

★ = New

Chapter 1

Grandmother's Cow

¡Hola (oh-lah)! I'm Ricardo, Judith's husband. My mother and father were born in Mexico. They immigrated to the United States before I was born. Do you know where I was born?

Who were the *immigrants* in Ricardo's family?

I would like to tell you my favorite story. It is one of Isabel and Daniel's favorite stories too. It is about an old cow and my grandmother.

My mother used to tell this story. She always started by saying, "In Mexico, when I was growing up, we had chickens and a few cows that just wandered around our houses."

Think about that! The animals could go wherever they wanted, whenever they wanted.

Mama would chuckle and say, "There was an old cow. That old cow always tried to come into your grandmother's house, but she would shoo it out. You should have seen Grandmother when that old cow showed up in the doorway.

"Grandmother would grab her frying pan and run toward the cow saying, 'Out, out, out.'

"Then the old cow would go, 'Moooo.' But she would not move.

"This would make Grandmother yell, 'Go, go, go,' until the cow finally moved."

Who told Ricardo this story? Where did the story take place? Why did Ricardo's mother chuckle when she told him this story?

My mother would end the story by chuckling and saying, "Oh, what a ruckus! After a while, the old cow would slowly walk off."

What do you think a ruckus is? Do you think the story is funny? Why or why not? Do you think Ricardo's grandmother lived in the country or in a city?

Daniel and Isabel like this story. It makes them laugh just like I laughed when my mother told me the story.

Whenever my mother talked about growing up in Mexico, she would smile and her eyes would glisten. But then she would look a little sad too. I think my mother missed Mexico.

INFERENCE

1. Why do you think Daniel and Isabel laugh when Ricardo tells this story?

INFERENCE

2. What makes this story funny?

DRAWING CONCLUSIONS

3. Ricardo's mother would smile but her eyes would glisten. Why would Ricardo's mother's eyes glisten?

INFERENCE

4. What makes this story bittersweet?

Chapter 2

A Visit to Mexico

¡Hola! It's Ricardo again. This story is about my mother, my grandmother, and me. When I was twelve, Mama took me to visit Mexico. When Daniel and Isabel are a little older, we also will visit Mexico.

Papa took Mama and me to the bus station. We were sad to leave Papa behind, but he had to work.

The trip to Mexico from the United States took many hours. The quiet rumbling of the bus made me drowsy. I slept for a long time. Finally, Mama shook me and said, "Ricardo, we are here!"

Why do you think the trip to Mexico made Ricardo *drowsy*? What do you think Ricardo will see in Mexico?

The bus came to a slow stop. I looked for cows and chickens, but there were none. There were many houses, stores, and people. It looked like the United States!

My grandmother had moved to the city to be near relatives. I would not meet the cow! We greeted her with hugs and kisses. In my best Spanish, I said, "Hi, Grandmother! How have you been? I like the color of your little house."

What do you think Ricardo is saying in Spanish?

We sat at the kitchen table. Grandmother gave us sweet bread and hot chocolate. I took a bite and said, "¡Qué delicioso!"

Grandmother smiled.

Spanish words flew back and forth. Mama said, "Do you remember that old cow?" We all laughed and laughed.

The seven days of our trip flew by. We visited relatives. We went to the market and walked through the stands. Everywhere we went, Mama waved at somebody and said, "¡Buenos días!"

Soon it was time to go home. I wanted to see Papa, but I was also sad to leave Grandmother.

Today, I make sweet bread and hot chocolate for Daniel and Isabel. When I smell the sweet bread baking, it is as if Abuela is standing beside me. It makes me feel both happy and sad.

What did Ricardo, his mother, and grandmother laugh about? Why is making sweet bread and hot chocolate bittersweet for Ricardo?

Think and Talk

1. Why do you think Ricardo is both happy and sad when he thinks about his grandmother?

INFERENCE

2. Do you think this story is bittersweet? Why or why not?

INFERENCE

3. When Ricardo smells sweet bread baking today, what do you think he thinks of?

Fluency

Fudge

One of Papa's favorite stories was about a   8
horse named Fudge. Papa would say, "When I   16
was little, my brothers and I rode horses every   25
day. I thought the horses on our ranch were   34
very big and powerful. My favorite horse was   42
Fudge."   43

Papa would say, "That big horse, Fudge,   50
had a short black mane. He was so big that I   61
had to climb on a ladder to get on his back. I   73
would try to grab his stubby little mane, and my   83
fingers would slip.   86

"Then Fudge would move! I fell many   93
times. I think that big horse was laughing   101
at me."   103

Papa would chuckle when he talked about   110
Fudge. There was a faraway look in his eyes.   119
Sometimes I think he even looked a little sad.   128

Who do you think is the narrator in this story? Who first told the story?
Where do you think it took place?

Glossary

advice

Advice is what someone tells others they should do.

If I have trouble getting up in the morning, what *advice* would you give me?

ancient

Ancient means very, very old. Something that is ancient may be thousands of years old.

The *ancient* buildings were falling down.

appreciate

Appreciate means to be thankful for something.

We *appreciate* the teachers because they help us learn new things.

brag

Brag means to talk proudly about things you own or things you've done.

Tom *bragged* about how strong he was.

contented

Contented means happy and satisfied with something.

After eating the luscious soup, the man was *contented*.

curious

Someone who is **curious** wants to know more about something.

Sandy was very *curious* about plants and wanted to learn more.

despite

Despite is another way to say "even though."

Despite taking a nap, I am still tired.

disappointed

Disappointed means to have a feeling of sadness when you don't get what you want.

When they couldn't go on the field trip, the children were *disappointed*.

drowsy

When you are **drowsy**, you are very sleepy.

If you are *drowsy*, you might want to take a nap.

embarrassed

Embarrassed means to be uncomfortable or nervous and worried about something you've done.

Tim was *embarrassed* when he dropped his lunch.

Glossary

emperor

An **emperor** is the leader of a country or countries.

Jun became *emperor* of all China.

folktale

A **folktale** is a story that people tell each other and pass along from one generation to the next.

"Stone Soup" is a *folktale* from England.

generation

Within a family, there are grand-parents, parents, and children. Each group is called a **generation**.

Your grandparents and their brothers and sisters are one *generation*.

glisten

Glisten means to sparkle or look shiny.

A diamond *glistens* in the sunlight.

imagine

Imagine means to make a picture of something in your mind. You can also imagine how something might smell, taste, and feel.

Imagine flying like a bird.

immigrate

Immigrate means to move to another country.

Maya's father *immigrated* to the United States from Costa Rica.

integrity

Integrity is complete honesty. A person who has integrity always tells the truth and does the right thing.

Maria showed *integrity* when she told her mom that she broke the window.

luscious

Luscious means delicious and mouth-watering. Something that is luscious has a delicious taste or smell.

The ripe peach was *luscious*.

merry

Merry means happy and cheerful.

As the boy skipped down the path, he whistled a *merry* tune.

minstrel

A **minstrel** is a person who lived long ago and traveled from place to place singing and playing music.

The *minstrel* is playing a fiddle.

Glossary

permission

Permission is being told that you can do something.

You should always ask your teacher for *permission* to bring a pet to school.

scarce

When something is **scarce**, there is not enough for everyone.

During the winter, food is *scarce* for the forest animals.

scrumptious

Scrumptious means delicious.

Something that is *scrumptious* tastes very, very good.

successor

A **successor** is the person who takes over someone's job.

Bill retired as the coach of the baseball team. The new coach is Grace. Grace is Bill's *successor.*

summon

Summon means to order someone to come to a place.

The Emperor *summoned* the people to the palace.

village

A **village** is like a town, but smaller. A village is a place where people live and work.

The people from the small mountain *village* came into town to buy things.

wealthy

Wealthy means to have a lot of something—usually money.

A *wealthy* person is someone who has a lot of money.

wonderful

Wonderful is another word for excellent, great, or fantastic.

The soup gave off a *wonderful* smell.

菜根飄香

法界食譜 1

素食的美味在於恬與悅

是恬靜的享受

是愉悅的滿足

Contents

菜根飄香

開味炒品　　　輕鬆拈來

殺生是世界戰爭的開始

無論哪一位，要是能不吃肉，
這就是幫助這個世界，令世界沒有戰爭。

殺生，包括自己殺，或者叫他人殺，或者見作隨喜，都包括在內了。我們人殺生是世界戰爭的一個開始，所以說：

千百年來碗裏羹　　冤深似海恨難平
欲知世上刀兵劫　　試聽屠門夜半聲

千百年以來，我們這一碗肉湯，羹就是羹湯，或者是牛肉的湯，或者是羊肉的湯，或者是豬肉的湯，或者是馬肉、驢肉、貓肉、狗肉等種種肉的湯。千百年以來，人吃許多眾生肉的湯，這叫千百年來碗裏羹。

冤深似海恨難平：這裏邊的冤氣好像海一樣，你殺我，我殺你，互相殺殺不已，不能停止。也就和看電影是一樣的道理，你殺我，我就殺你。你殺我，吃我的肉；我若殺你的時候，又吃你的肉，互相來吃肉。你吃我的肉時，我覺得很痛苦，而你覺得很快樂；等我吃你的肉時，你又覺得很痛苦，但我覺得很快樂。這個世間就是這麼果報循環，循環不已。這個冤，冤就是怨仇，就像海那麼深的仇恨，所以不容易把它平下來，總是有一個深深的坑在那兒，深深地不平，所以恨難平。

欲知世上刀兵劫：世界上各國作戰殺人，你殺我、我殺你，這個國家用軍隊去和那個國家作戰，放槍、放砲，殺了很多人，這叫刀兵劫。你如果想要知道世上在戰爭裏死去的人的因緣，為什麼有刀兵這個劫數──

試聽屠門夜半聲：你應該聽一聽殺豬那個地方、殺牛那個地方、殺羊那個地方，那兒半夜是什麼聲音！半夜時，豬也哭、牛也哭、羊也哭。牠們在那兒哭，說：「啊！你就要來殺我了，我將來一定也要殺你的！」這互相殺，殺殺不已，殺來殺去。

所以我們無論哪一位，要是能不吃肉，這就是幫助世界，令世界沒有戰爭；你若吃肉，就會造成世界大戰爭，那時就會死很多人。我們大家都應該瞭解這種的情形，所以要是想世界上沒有戰爭，就是不吃眾生肉。我們能維持這個身體生存就可以了，不需要胖得太厲害，也不需要叫它吃得太好了。既然這樣，我們不要貪口腹，而殺一切眾生的生命。

──── **宣化上人**

編者的話

《漢書》云：「民以食為天。」食物，一直是大家感興趣的話題。孔子曰：「色惡不食，臭惡不食，不時不食，割不正不食。」然而，可曾想過我們為什麼要吃食物？要怎麼選擇食物？

佛教將食物稱為藥石，在中國醫學發展的早期，以飲食來治病是很重要的療法，中醫裏的湯劑，原指烹調的湯水。在中國最早的醫學論著《素問》中很少提及藥物，卻頻頻涉及飲食調養。

因此，我們用餐目的不僅在於延續生命，更要有強健的身體，如此方能實踐我們的理想，乃至於對生活週遭的環境有所貢獻，而人類的理想即建立於對生命的尊重。然而，隨著科技與知識的發達，烹飪食物的技術花樣百出，食物本身的季節性與地域性也越來越薄弱。食物的原始意義，似乎已被淡忘。

所謂「健康的吃」，是全面性的，是身心靈同時兼顧的。《禮記》載：「食肉勇敢而悍，食穀智慧而巧。」食物可以使身體感官愉悅，思想純淨與延續慧命。古人將各種飲食的味道歸納為五種：酸、甜、苦、辣、鹹，不同的調味可強化我們的內臟。中國人常說「吃什麼，補什麼」，英文也說：「You are what you eat.」也就是吃什麼，像什麼。可是，沒有人願意像豬或像雞！

佛教說「眾生平等」，我們既然不會吃自己的家人，當然也不會吃地球村中的鄰居。「無緣大慈，同體大悲」，說的就是沒有分別心與感同身受，有了如此的意念於食物之中，我們的思想會更趨於平靜、安祥，我們的慧命也會得到更多的滋長。

正因如此，本會推出一系列的法界食譜。《菜根飄香》是一本適合「上班族」與「easy 族」的飲食寶典，其中簡單易買的食材，搭配最基本的料理，輕易煮出色香味俱全的佳餚，使初學者或上班族在忙碌的一天之後，也可以輕鬆享用均衡的飲食！書中收有 58 道美味易煮的佳餚，讓您吃得健康又愉快。

《大方廣佛華嚴經》云：「香積世界，餐香飯而三昧顯。」所以法界食譜第二集，命名為《香積世界》，書中提供六十多道功夫菜，色香味俱全，希望藉此能讓您吃得「餐香飯而三昧顯」。

道場中的果觀師兄，曾是烹飪界無人不曉的大師傅，兩位蔣故總統與多位政要名流都相當喜歡吃他烹調的菜。果觀師兄因緣際會，皈依了宣化上人，從此不沾葷腥，致力於推廣素食。所以法界食譜第三集《御廚果觀》，收錄 60 道左右果觀師兄的獨門私房菜，讓您體驗素食料理的自在變化。

秉持 宣化上人「不爭、不貪、不求、不自私、不自利、不打妄語」、「凍死不攀緣、餓死不化緣、窮死不求緣」的精神。我們在硬體條件極差的情況下，憑著供養、戒殺、放生的心，決定出版食譜。齋堂的一角放著幾盞書桌型檯燈、幾塊布頭、一架數位相機，就成了所謂的攝影棚。香積組的義工們，將平日法會中供眾與個人拿手的菜餚烹調出來，歡喜地烹煮出來，綴以小花、蔬葉，成就了一道道天廚妙供。

「吃素」是祈求世界和平最直接的方法，因為「千百年來碗裏羹，冤深似海恨難平；欲知世上刀兵劫，但聽屠門夜半聲。」願以「法界食譜」此一系列的出版，喚醒世人對生命的尊重，長養人類對眾生的慈悲。

下面提供一些烹調 祕笈 希望對您有幫助！

法界菜餚的特色，儘量採取天然的食材，低油、低鹽、少糖、無蔥、無蒜、無蛋、無奶、無味素、少素塊（黃豆製品），是我們堅持的原則，希望大家都能吃得健康、吃得法喜充滿。

書內所標示的份量、用量，僅供參考，讀者可依個人的體質、身體健康狀況、與喜好來增減，適度用之。（調味料也會依產牌不同，其鹹淡甜度也有所不同。）

通常在作菜時，不外乎是以色、香、味、菜性、刀工等的配合。
色──大約可分：紅如紅蘿蔔、紅辣椒、甜椒、紅番茄等，黃如竹筍、黃甜椒、黃番茄等，綠如各式綠色蔬菜等，白如白蘿蔔、茭白筍、大頭菜、白木耳等，黑如香菇、黑木耳、海帶等，紫如紫高麗、茄子、紫蘇、紫色地瓜葉等。

香──如麻油、八角、胡椒、花椒、桂皮、香椿、香菜、芹菜、薑等。

味──如鹽、糖、醬油、醋、味噌、豆豉、番茄醬、咖哩粉等。

至於菜性，通常涼性的菜，諸如苦瓜、冬瓜、絲瓜、白蘿蔔、大白菜等，可以加香菇、薑、麻油等入味調理，使其中性化。

在配菜、切菜時，刀工是不可少的，可略分為長、圓、方、絲、大、小等刀法。一般視食材的形狀來配合刀法：長配長、圓配圓、方配方、絲配絲…即可。

您若是初習烹飪者，開始也許會不盡如意，但只要多接觸、多做幾次，一定可以煮出自己料想不到的好效果。好了，請翻開下一頁，準備動手做做看吧！

法界食譜工作群

食法
譜界

食 材簡介

（壹）時令蔬菜

（貳）常用根莖類及瓜類蔬菜基本處理

（參）常用粉類基本用途簡介

（壹）時令蔬菜

冬春季：根莖類——白蘿蔔、紅蘿蔔、馬鈴薯、地瓜、豆薯、牛蒡、大頭菜（結頭菜）。

結球類——高麗菜、卷心大白菜、卷心萵苣、花椰菜、番茄。

葉菜類——芥菜、甘藍菜、大菜心、龍鬚菜、青江菜、菠菜、豌豆苗、小白菜、萵苣生菜類（A 菜類）、地瓜葉、芹菜、甜菜、白鳳菜、紅鳳菜。

夏秋季：根莖類——蓮藕、蓮子、竹筍（麻竹筍、桂竹筍、綠竹筍、蘆筍、茭白筍）、芋頭、嫩薑、老薑。

瓜　類——絲瓜、冬瓜、苦瓜、大黃瓜、小黃瓜、南瓜、瓠瓜。

豆　類——四季豆（敏豆）、豇豆（長豆、豆角）、秋葵、綠豆、紅豆、花生、豌豆、豌豆仁（青豆仁）、甜豆。

葉菜類——莧菜、空心菜。

四季：綠豆芽、黃豆芽、地瓜葉、菌類（草菇、金針菇、鮮香菇、鮑魚菇、杏鮑菇、秀珍菇、美白菇、鴻禧菇…）、木耳、海帶（海帶、海帶芽、海帶根）…

大豆、小麥類製品：

豆腐、豆干、油豆腐、 豆包

豆條、麵筋條、麵筋糰

百頁、麵輪、麵卷（油皮）

麵筋袋 、干絲

（貳） 常用根莖類及瓜類蔬菜基本處理

1. 白蘿蔔：去不去皮皆可，熟食、生食兩相宜。
2. 紅蘿蔔：去不去皮皆可，熟食、生食兩相宜。最好是加油、海鹽同煮後食用，其維生素才釋放出來。
3. 馬鈴薯：去不去皮皆可，熟食。（若長芽不可食）
4. 地瓜：去不去皮皆可，熟食。
5. 豆薯（刈薯）：去皮後使用，熟食、生食兩相宜。
6. 牛蒡：去不去皮皆可，熟食。
7. 筍類（麻竹筍、桂竹筍、綠竹筍、蘆筍、茭白筍）：去外殼後使用，熟食。
8. 大頭菜（結頭菜）：去皮後使用，熟食、生食兩相宜。
9. 蓮藕：去不去皮皆可，熟食、或汆燙後涼拌。
10. 蓮子：直接煮即可，熟食。
11. 菜心：去不去皮皆可，熟食、生食兩相宜。
12. 芋頭：去皮後使用，熟食。
13. 嫩薑：不去皮。
14. 老薑：去不去皮皆可。
15. 絲瓜：去皮後使用。
16. 冬瓜：去皮、去籽後使用，熟食。
17. 苦瓜：不去皮，可直接食用（內有籽，可去籽；亦可不拿掉同煮，但籽不吃），生食或熟食皆可。
18. 大黃瓜：去不去皮皆可，可直接食用（內有籽，拿不拿掉均可），熟食、生食兩相宜。
19. 小黃瓜：不去皮，可直接食用，熟食、生食兩相宜，或做泡菜用。
20. 南瓜：去不去皮皆可，可直接使用（內有籽，拿不拿掉均可），熟食。
21. 瓠瓜（瓢瓜）：去皮後使用，熟食。

（參）常用粉類基本用途簡介

麵　粉：全麥麵粉——適用於比較粗纖維質之麵食類，如全麥饅頭、麵包、麵條、餅乾等…。

　　　　高筋麵粉——適用於比較有彈性，有嚼勁的麵食類，如饅頭、麵包、麵條…。

　　　　中筋麵粉——適用於不需要太有彈性的點心類，如包子、水餃皮、或炒熟作濃湯時勾芡用…。

　　　　低筋麵粉——適用於完全不需要彈性的點心類，如糕點類製作…。

太白粉：可用於勾芡，或製作點心用，透明有彈性，待涼時容易凝結成硬塊。

地瓜粉：可用於勾芡，或製作點心用，半透明有彈性，待涼時凝結成塊。

玉米粉：可用於勾芡，或製作點心用，透明有彈性，滑嫩，待涼時仍有彈性，比較不會成硬塊之感。

葛根粉：可用於勾芡，或製作點心用，透明有彈性，滑嫩，待涼時仍有彈性，比較不會成硬塊之感，價位高，對健康佳。

蓮藕粉：可用於勾芡，或製作點心用，透明有彈性，滑嫩，待涼時仍有彈性，比較不會成硬塊之感，價位高，對健康佳。

蒟蒻粉：可用於製作蒟蒻塊、果凍、甜食點心類。低卡食品。

膠凍粉（果凍粉）：是海藻萃取物。可製作茶凍、果凍、點心類…。

烹

飪基礎

(壹) 烹飪習慣用語、份量簡介

清洗材料：材料用水洗淨，通常青菜要換三次水，並瀝乾水份備用。蔬菜如何清洗最為安全而乾淨？以大量清水沖洗蔬菜最好（尤其是生食蔬果、芽菜類，最好是直接在水龍頭下沖洗）。小葉菜類應先接近根處切根，把葉片張開後沖洗；包葉菜類應於去除外葉後，再拆成單片沖洗。根莖菜類應先清洗後再行去皮，凹陷不平處宜削厚一點，以除去可能附著表皮的農藥及污垢。花果菜類連皮食用者，可用軟毛刷刷洗；易沈積農藥的部位，如凹陷的果蒂處，宜先切除再行沖洗。

註：買回來的菜，打開放置於外面一天一夜，整理後，裝於保鮮盒內才放入冰箱，可
　　減少殘留之農藥等物質，及保鮮等。若葉菜類會變比較乾燥，於使用前用水泡即
　　可回復。

氽燙：把材料放入沸水中，用大火煮開，或菜變成翠綠色，即撈起立刻入冷水（或冷
　　　開水中）漂涼，隨後撈起瀝乾。可直接食用或再烹調時以保持菜色，並燙去澀
　　　味，及一些在食物中所殘留的物質，即是氽燙的作用。（直接食用，若必須經
　　　過漂涼時，務必用冷開水。）
炒：把食物放入炒菜鍋內，翻攪到熟，就是炒。
煮：把食物放入炒菜鍋內，翻攪後加入少量的水，繼續煮熟，就是煮。
燜煮：把食物放入炒菜鍋內，翻攪後加入適量的水，蓋上鍋蓋，用小火煮熟，就是燜
　　　煮。（所謂適量：即視材料之多寡，調節所需之水量。）
燉：把食物裝入器皿中，再將器皿放入有水的鍋內，蓋上鍋蓋，用小火
　　使食物熟透，就是燉。
蒸：把食物裝入蒸籠或器皿中，放入沸水的鍋內，蓋
　　上蓋子，用大火使食物熟透，就是蒸。（如蒸包
　　子或饅頭的時候，水量要多一點，火要大，水蒸
　　氣上來的越多，蒸出來的口感越好。但應視食物
　　之需要而決定火的大小。）
燴：在食物煮熟後並有菜汁的食物中，淋上芡汁，就
　　是燴。
炸：把食物放入較多量的沸油中，使之熟，就是炸。
煎：把食物放入少油的鍋內，使之熟，就是煎。

勾芡（芡汁）：在食物烹調即將完成，還未起鍋前，將調好的玉米粉水（視需要之粉類）
　　　　　　　徐徐倒入，並一邊攪動，將所有食材成粘稠、或成濃汁，且成透明狀，
　　　　　　　即勾芡完成。（用玉米粉、太白粉、地瓜粉、或麵粉，可視需要而定，
　　　　　　　水的比例約 1：3，水比粉多。）
薄芡：在煮沸的湯內或仍有湯汁的菜內，用少許的芡汁淋入，並邊淋邊拌均勻，看似有似
　　　無，湯汁只有一點點的濃度即是。

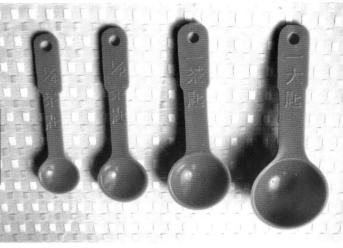

1 台斤 = 600 公克
1 台兩 = 37.5 公克
1 公斤 = 1000 公克 = 1 台斤又 10 兩半
1　　磅 = 450 公克

1 大匙 = 15cc =1 湯匙
1 茶匙 = 5cc = 1/3 湯匙
1/2 茶匙 = 2.5cc = 1/6 湯匙
1/4 茶匙 = 1.25cc = 1/12 湯匙

1 杯 （電鍋杯） = 180cc

(貳) 素高湯：

1

材　料：　甘蔗 30 公分、黃豆芽 600 公克（1 台斤）
　　　　　紅蘿蔔 1 條、乾香菇 3 朵、海帶 30 公分

步　驟：1. 將所有材料洗淨切大塊，入鍋加水（蓋過材
　　　　　料的量）蓋上鍋蓋大火煮開，改小文火燜煮
　　　　　約 50～60 分鐘。

　　　　2. 瀝掉所有菜渣，即成高湯。（菜渣可加入調
　　　　　味料後食用。）

2

材　料：　海帶 30 公分、大頭菜(結頭菜)1 個

步　驟：1. 海帶洗淨，切約 5 公分寬。大頭
　　　　　菜去皮切大塊，入鍋加水（蓋過
　　　　　材料的量），蓋上鍋蓋大火煮
　　　　　開，改小文火燜煮約 50～60 分
　　　　　鐘。

　　　　2. 瀝掉所有菜渣，即成高湯。（菜
　　　　　渣加入調味料後，仍可食用。）

材　料：　香菇 5 朵、白蘿蔔 1 條

步　驟：1. 香菇洗淨，對切。白蘿蔔去皮切
　　　　　大塊，入鍋加水（蓋過材料的
　　　　　量），蓋上鍋蓋，大火煮開，改
　　　　　小文火燜煮約 50～60 分鐘。

　　　　2. 瀝掉所有菜渣，即成高湯。（菜
　　　　　渣加入調味料後，仍可食用。）

3

4

材　料：　甘蔗 30 公分、黃豆芽 600 公克（1 台斤）
　　　　　海帶 30 公分、紅蘿蔔 1 條、高麗菜 1 個

步　驟：1. 將所有材料洗淨切大塊，入鍋加水（蓋過
　　　　　材料的量）蓋上鍋蓋，大火煮開，改小文
　　　　　火燜煮約 50～60 分鐘。

　　　　2. 瀝掉所有菜渣，即成高湯。（菜渣加入調
　　　　　味料後，仍可食用。）

高湯用途：適用於任何烹煮過程中所需要的湯頭。

變　化：1. 在烹調過程中，如果用此高湯，可以不用再加糖或味精等的調味料，煮出來的菜餚美味
　　　　　又健康。不妨自己動手做做看，是極天然的甘甜味。

　　　　2. 一次準備不妨份量多一些，待涼後分裝放入冷凍庫貯存。需要時取出解凍，加入菜餚或
　　　　　當湯底，可增加口感與風味。

　　　　3. 材料可以隨個人喜好的口味，自由變化、搭配。

(參)素醬：

材　　料：　五香豆干 5 塊、香菇 5 朵、小麥胚芽 1 杯、全麥麵粉 1 杯
　　　　　　埃及豆（雪蓮子）1 杯

調味料：　天然醬油 3 大匙、粗味噌（或豆瓣醬）1 碗、紅糖半碗

步　　驟：1. 豆干洗淨、香菇洗淨泡軟擠乾水份，都切細末。埃及豆洗淨泡一夜，
　　　　　　　瀝乾水份，入電鍋蒸熟，趁熱搗碎。小麥胚芽、麵粉分開炒香。

　　　　　2. 油入炒鍋，待熱加入豆干末，炒至金黃色，加入香菇末，再炒香，
　　　　　　　入醬油炒香，加入所有材料、水（蓋過所有材料）及調味料，用小
　　　　　　　文火燜煮約 30 分鐘即成。

　　　　　3. 待涼可分小包裝，入冷凍庫（約可保存一個月），需食用時取出
　　　　　　　加熱即可。

用　　途：　適用於拌麵、拌飯、拌菜。

(一) 麵輪：

材　料：麵筋條　（如圖）

步　驟：麵筋條切 1 公分厚圓片，入油鍋炸成金黃色，
　　　　撈起，瀝乾油份，即成麵輪（如圖）。待涼，
　　　　入密封袋放入冷凍庫冷凍（可保存約一個月），
　　　　供需要時隨時取用。

用　途：烹煮油飯、燉補湯、配根莖菜類紅燒用。

秘　訣：可用少量油，分次炸完。

(二) 油皮：

材　料：麵筋條　（如圖）

步　驟：麵筋條撕成大片狀，入油鍋炸成金黃色，撈
　　　　起，瀝乾油份，即成油皮（或稱麵卷，如圖）。
　　　　待涼，入密封袋，放入冷凍庫冷凍（可保存約
　　　　一個月），供需要時隨時取用。

用　途：烹煮油飯、燉補湯、配根莖菜類紅燒用。

秘　訣：可用少量油，分次炸完。

（三） 麵筋糰：

材　料：麵筋糰（如圖）

步　驟：麵筋糰用手掰開大小適中，入油鍋炸成金黃色，撈起，瀝乾油份即成。待涼，入密封袋，放入冷凍庫冷凍（可保存約一個月），供需要時隨時取用。

用　途：烹煮油飯、燉補湯、配根莖菜類紅燒用。

秘　訣：1.油炸時要用中低油溫，慢慢地炸，比較能炸到裏外透徹、乾酥，成品也比較不容易腐壞。

　　　　2.可用少量油，分次炸完。

（四） 麵筋袋：

材　料：麵筋袋（如圖）

步　驟：麵筋袋對切再對切，或再小一點，大小可隨喜，入油鍋炸成金黃色，撈起，瀝乾油份即成。待涼，入密封袋，放入冷凍庫冷凍（可保存約一個月），供需要時隨時取用。

用　途：可搭配各種根莖類、海帶等紅燒，或單獨作滷味，或搭配葉菜類炒。

秘　訣：可用少量油，分次炸完。

（五）豆包之處理：

甲、紫菜豆包捲：

材　料： 優質厚豆包600公克（1台斤）、紫菜片2片
　　　　　乾豆皮1張（半圓）（此材料可作成2份）

調味料： 油膏1大匙、胡椒粉1/2茶匙、麻油1大匙、糖1/2茶匙、海鹽1/2茶匙、麵糊：麵粉1大匙加水1大匙拌均勻

步　驟： 1.豆包撕成小碎絲，入所有的調味料，並充份拌均勻備用。
　　　　　2.乾豆皮剪成兩張，一張置於最低層：上面放一片紫菜片鋪好，將作法1.取一半，平鋪在上面，捲起（如春捲）沾麵糊封口（另一份作法相同），放入已抹油的平盤內，入蒸鍋，用小文火蒸約20分鐘。待涼，入密封袋，放入冷凍庫冷凍（可保存約一個月），供需要時隨時取用。

用　途： 乾煎、油炸、或烤後，可切片直接食用，或可作成糖醋，或用醬油作成醬味兩種口味，無論是家常、或宴客皆適宜。

秘　訣： 1.捲起來的時候，稍為用點力，可以捲緊一點，在切開時比較不易散開。
　　　　　2.入鍋蒸時，要用小文火蒸，若用中大火蒸，會裂開。
　　　　　3.蒸完後取出，要待涼後，方可作後續處理，否則會散開，較不易成形。
　　　　　4.入油鍋炸時，要用小火炸，才不會裂開。

乙、炸豆包：

材　料： 豆包

步　驟： 豆包整片入油鍋炸成金黃色，撈起，瀝乾油份即成。待涼，入密封袋，放入冷凍庫冷凍，可保存約一個月，供需要時隨時取用。

用　途： 炒麵、炒米粉、炒青菜等…。

（六）蒟蒻塊之製作

材　料：　蒟蒻粉 37.5 公克（1 台兩）、鹼粉 1/4 茶匙、水 850cc、白醋 1 大匙、海鹽 1 茶匙

步　驟：　水放入鍋內，將鹼粉徐徐倒入，用筷子攪拌均勻，再徐徐倒入蒟蒻粉，用筷子攪拌均勻，再繼續攪拌至呈稀糊狀再倒入平盤內，端起平盤抖動，使之充實，室溫放置 2 小時（或不用先放置 2 小時，立刻放入蒸鍋內，用小文火蒸 30 分鐘），取出，切大塊（或視自己需要之大小），再放入鍋內加水煮，以小火煮約 10 分鐘，再換一次水加白醋及海鹽煮 30 分鐘即可。

用　途：　可當涼拌菜、炒菜、紅燒、滷味。

秘　訣：1. 攪拌時，要同一方向，例如順時鐘，比較不會有空氣，而有細緻感。

　　　　2. 倒入平盤時，再端起抖動，會更充實不含空氣。

　　　　3. 蒸或煮的時候，要用小火，成品較細緻感。

1

2-1

（七）基本發麵：

材　料：1. 全麥麵粉 300 公克（半台斤）、中筋麵粉 300 公克（半台斤）
　　　　紅糖 1 大匙、海鹽少許。
　　　　2. 酵母粉 1 大匙、溫水（約 40 度）2 杯半。

步　驟：1. 取筷子一雙備用。**A.** 將材料 1. 全部放入盆中，攪拌均勻。
　　　　　　　　　　　　　　B. 將材料 2. 放入大碗中攪拌均勻備用。
　　　　2. 將 **B.** 之酵母水徐徐倒入 **A.** 之麵粉中間，並邊用筷子在麵粉盆的
　　　　中間攪拌均勻後（如圖一），用蓋子或濕布蓋上。待其發酵至兩
　　　　倍高（如圖二），再將其餘麵粉揉入，至表面平滑後（如圖三），
　　　　用蓋子或濕布蓋上。待其發酵至兩倍大（如圖四），即可取出分
　　　　成需要之等份，包入餡料作包子、餡餅、雜糧饅頭、全麥饅頭等
　　　　…，用途廣泛。

註：此發麵法可使發酵加速，發成的麵，效果既細緻又有彈性，且味甘美。

2-2

3

4

（八）豆沙之製作：

材　料：　紅豆600公克（1台斤）、原味冰糖300公克（半台斤）

步　驟：　紅豆洗淨，泡一夜（或4小時），加水一倍，用大火煮滾，改
　　　　　小文火燜煮1小時（查看是否已熟爛透，若未達到，再繼續煮），
　　　　　倒入炒鍋，加入冰糖，不停翻炒至糖化、水乾即成。待涼，分
　　　　　裝入冷凍庫冷凍。需要時，取出退冰即可使用。

用　途：　可當豆沙包、甜食之餡料。

變　化：　1.紅豆亦可改其他的豆類，可依個人需要更換。煮紅豆時，一定
　　　　　要使之達到熟爛之程度，才能加入糖，否則會變成顆粒狀。

　　　　　2.做綠豆沙時，若不喜有雜質感，可用綠豆仁，效果更佳。

開 味妙品

Bon Appetite

舌在胃前頭
味開胃也開
胃開營養來
迎接好未來

時時念佛 日日吃素 年年戒殺 月月放生

——宣化上人

  開味妙品

糖 醋 泡 菜

步　驟：
1. 洗淨所有材料，瀝乾水份，切 1 公分大丁，用海鹽、薑片醃至軟，用冷開水洗後，撈起瀝乾水份。
2. 將步驟 1.加入冰糖、檸檬汁醃一天即可食用。

變　化：
白菜，高麗菜、豆角（長豆）、西洋芹菜、紅蘿蔔、蓮藕、大頭菜、白花椰菜、茄子都可以製成相當美味的泡菜。

知　識：
經自然醱酵的泡菜，因密封漬製，抑制了不良微生物的活動，而產生了豐富的乳酸菌，乳酸菌醱酵產生乳酸、醋酸、醇、酯、胺基酸等，形成酸味與芳香的美味，營養成分高，維他命損失少，是一道有益人體健康之菜餚。

材　料：
白蘿蔔 1 條
小黃瓜 2 條

調味料：
嫩薑片 1 碗
冰糖 1 碗
檸檬汁 1 碗
海鹽 1 大匙

儒教周易有言，乾曰大生，坤曰廣生，
天地之大德曰生，故孔子讚易以生生。
吾人應體天地好生之德，提倡戒殺放生。

——圓瑛法師

  開味妙品

味噌蕪菁

步　驟： 1. 調味料全部加在一起拌均勻備用。結頭菜去皮洗淨擦乾，切約 0.3 公分薄片。蘋果（連皮）亦切成同樣大小。

2. 將步驟 1. 全部放入碗中拌均勻即可食用。（醃泡 1 小時會更入味）

秘　訣： 1. 切結頭菜、葡萄柚時，砧板及壓汁器也要擦乾，醃漬以後保存較久。放入冰箱，約可保存一星期。

2. 漬製泡菜取食的時候，要用乾淨的筷子夾取。如果生水或不淨的筷箸進入泡菜罐內，泡菜的漬汁就會變質。

知　識： 味噌蕪菁原為日本著名湯品，亦可製成涼拌菜。喜愛美食的北宋文學家蘇東坡，有道出名的東坡羹，就是將大白菜、蕪菁、蘿蔔等加上生米去煮，類似什錦蔬菜粥的做法，很受歡迎。

材　料：
大頭菜（結頭菜）1 顆
有機蘋果 1 個

調味料：
有機味噌半杯
糖 1/2 茶匙
葡萄柚汁 1 杯

時時佛光普照　日日如意吉祥
月月福慧雙增　年年壽祿無量

——宣化上人

開味妙品

清涼絲拌

（約 4～6 人份）

步　驟： 1. 海帶絲洗淨汆燙。調味料加在一起調均勻備用。
　　　　 2. 用餐前，將所有的材料及調味料拌在一起即可食用。

秘　訣： 海帶汆燙時，加些醋，可軟化、去腥。

變　化： 也可以海帶芽替換，口感佳。

知　識： 海帶又稱昆布。含豐富的蛋白質、碘、鈣、磷、鐵、
　　　　 維他命 B1、維他命 B2、維他命 C 和 A；是典型的鹼
　　　　 性食物，對保持人體血液呈正常的弱鹼性很有幫助，
　　　　 也是甲狀腺腫大、高血壓、冠心病患者的食療佳品。

材　料：
海帶絲 300 公克（半台斤）
小黃瓜絲 1 碗（2 條）
紅蘿蔔絲少許

調味料：
淡色醬油 1 大匙
小麻油 1/4 茶匙
糖 1 大匙
檸檬汁 1 大匙
嫩薑絲 2 大匙
烏醋 1 大匙

莫謂眾命微　沉溺而不援
應知惻隱心　是爲仁之端

　　　　　　　　　　——弘一大師

32　開味妙品

香炒花生

步　驟：
1. 花生洗淨，瀝乾水份。
2. 將海鹽入炒鍋，用中小火，放入花生，不停的翻炒，至花生表皮變色，並感覺較堅硬、清脆聲，起鍋，篩去鹽，待涼，即可食用。

秘　訣： 若是初次炒花生者，可以先用小火慢慢炒，待有經驗時，再用中火炒。用中火炒，要不停的翻動，一刻不得停，一直炒到比較輕手、有清脆聲的感覺時，即可起鍋。

變　化： 喜歡有點鹹味時，花生洗淨撈起，直接入炒鍋炒，帶點水份，使海鹽入味。

知　識： 常吃花生可保健康，故又稱為「長生果」。花生的營養價值很高，含有脂肪質、蛋白質、磷質、鈣質、鐵質，以及維他命 A、B，更含有促進血液凝固的成份（花生皮含此種成份較多）。養顏潤膚，治腳氣病和止血。

材　料：
生花生 600 公克（1 台斤）

調味料：
海鹽 1 碗

晓露零香粉　春風拂畫衣　輕纨原在手　未忍撲雙飛

————清·熊澹仙

　開味妙品

蔔乾豆腐

（約 4～6 人份）

步　驟： 1. 洗淨材料，瀝乾水份。豆腐招碎，瀝乾水份備用。
　　　　 2. 油 2 大匙入炒鍋，將蘿蔔乾末、碎豆腐同時入鍋，炒至香味出，加入糖、醬油、五香粉拌均勻，即可起鍋。

秘　訣： 豆腐的水份要乾再炒，比較容易炒出味道。

變　化： 可加入少許芹菜末、紅蘿蔔末，會有不同的美味。

知　識： 蘿蔔內含蛋白質、脂肪、糖分及鈣、磷、鐵等營養成分，維他命C含量較高，並含一種澱粉分解酵素，對人體吸收營養頗為有益。蘿蔔性味甘淡、補脾而不滯，俗云：「蘿蔔上市，醫生無事」，因為蘿蔔具有消炎、防暑、開胃等醫藥功能。

材　料：
蘿蔔乾末 1 碗
老豆腐 1 塊

調味料：
糖少許
醬油 1 茶匙
五香粉少許

上帝所創造的，即使是最低等的動物，
皆是生命合唱團的一員。

—— 林肯(Abraham Lincoln)

懷 古 豆 豉

（約 4～6 人份）

步　驟： 1. 豆豉洗淨，瀝乾水份。
2. 油入炒鍋待熱，放入薑末炒香，加入豆豉、糖，再
炒香即可起鍋。

秘　訣： 乾豆豉至少要洗五次以上，把外皮（表皮含有霉）
洗掉效果較佳。

變　化： 也可以加入蘿蔔乾、豆干丁等。或豆豉、薑末炒蘿
蔔乾；或豆豉、薑末炒豆干丁，其他步驟同，可任
意變化。

知　識： 豆豉是大豆的釀造製品。日本科學家指出：常以服
用豆豉，可防治食物中毒和腸道疾病，並認為豆豉
有助消化、防疾病、減慢老化、增強腦力、提高肝
臟解毒功能、防治高血壓、消除疲勞、預防癌症等
好處。然豆豉的食鹽含量高，要注意此點。

材　料：
乾豆豉 1 碗
薑末 1 大匙

調味料：
糖 1/2 茶匙

我認為素食者的人生態度，乃是出自極單純的生理上平衡狀態，因此對於人類的理想是有所裨益的。

—— 愛因斯坦(Albert Einstein)

甘鹹花生

（約 4～6 人份）

步　　驟：　花生洗淨，加一倍水，煮滾，倒掉水，再加一倍水、
　　　　　　八角、檸檬汁、醬油，用大火煮開，用小火燜煮至
　　　　　　花生熟透（約 1 小時）即成。（若鹹度不夠，再加
　　　　　　少許海鹽。）

秘　　訣：　花生務必煮至熟透。可招一招，感覺很爛，才可加
　　　　　　海鹽；若仍未爛的感覺加入海鹽，會使花生變得更
　　　　　　生硬。

變　　化：　可以用黑豆換個口味，並加入少許海帶同煮會更佳。

知　　識：　花生營養豐富，熱量大大高於肉類，比牛奶高 1 倍，
　　　　　　比雞蛋高 4 倍，且容易被人體吸收。用油煎、炸或
　　　　　　爆炒花生，對花生中富含的維他命 E 及其營養成分
　　　　　　破壞很大。中醫認為花生有悅脾和胃、潤肺化痰、
　　　　　　調氣養血，利水消腫、止血生乳之效。

材　　料：
生花生 300 公克（半台斤）

調味料：
八角 3 粒
檸檬汁 1 大匙
醬油 2 大匙

血肉淋漓味足珍　一般痛苦怨難伸
設身處地捫心想　誰肯將刀割自身

——宋・陸游

40　開味妙品

養生紫菜醬

（約 4～6 人份）

步　驟：　1. 將紫菜剪成 2 公分寬，用水洗淨，撈起瀝乾水份。
　　　　　 2. 水入鍋煮開，放入紫菜絲汆燙，撈起瀝乾水份，加入調味料，拌均勻即可食用。

秘　訣：　在汆燙後，水瀝得越乾越好，加入調味料後，口感好。

變　化：　也可以用海帶芽試一試。

知　識：　紫菜含豐富的蛋白質、碘、鈣、磷、鐵、硒及維他命 A、C、葉酸、葉綠素等，有「微量元素寶庫」之稱。中醫認為紫菜味甘鹹、性寒，能化痰、清熱利尿。紫菜是高蛋白、低脂肪、多礦物質、多維他命的理想食材。

材　料：
無沙乾紫菜 1 片

調味料：
醬油 1 茶匙
糖 1 茶匙
白醋 1 茶匙

任何確實的實驗都說明，任何一種生理或心理的疾病
都能靠吃素和喝純水而減輕病情。

　　　　　　　　—— 雪萊(Percy Bysshe Shelley，英國著名詩人)

開味妙品

家鄉酸菜

（約 4～6 人份）

步　驟： 1. 材料洗淨。酸菜切細丁，擠乾水份。辣椒切細丁。
2. 油一大匙入炒鍋，放入辣椒炒香，加入醬油，待醬油滾，即放入酸菜、糖，用小火炒至水份乾即成。

秘　訣： 只要炒到水份乾就可以，不必另外加水。

變　化： 炒雪裡紅亦可用此法。

知　識： 酸菜不但能增進食欲、幫助消化，而且還可以促進鐵元素的吸收。吃酸菜時，要多吃含維他命 C 豐富的新鮮蔬菜，維他命 C 能與亞硝酸鹽發生還原反應，阻止致癌物質的生成。有兩種酸菜絕不能吃：一是已變味或黴變的酸菜，二是沒醃透的酸菜，都可能致癌。

材　料：
酸菜（鹹菜）600 公克
小紅辣椒 2 個

調味料：
醬油 1 大匙
糖少許

食肉勇敢而悍，食穀智慧而巧。——《大戴禮記》

涼拌珊瑚

（約 4~6 人份）

步　驟：
1. 乾珊瑚草洗淨，用冷水泡開（約泡 3 小時，並換水 1~2 次），撈起，瀝乾水份，剪小段備用。小黃瓜洗淨切絲，拌入 1/2 茶匙海鹽，醃 10 分鐘，擠乾水份。
2. 步驟 1.及所有的調味料加入混合拌均勻，洒少許香油即成。

秘　訣：
檸檬汁酸，會使綠色小黃瓜的外皮變色，在食用前再加入，顏色比較翠綠。珊瑚草遇熱，即會產生粘稠狀。

變　化：
1. 喜歡軟一點，可以多泡一點時間。
2. 亦可作成珊瑚草果凍或冰糖海燕窩，作法請參閱本會出版的《香積世界》食譜。

知　識：
1. 珊瑚草又稱麒麟草、海鹽草、神草、福草，被當成不老長壽的天然食物。只生長在紅潮地帶，完全無污染純淨海域。含有豐富礦物質、植物性膠質、高纖、高鈣、高鐵及多種維他命，因此而得海底燕窩之美名。亦稱珊瑚鈣。本草記載之海鹽草就是珊瑚草。
2. 購買時要注意品質好的珊瑚草。若含有臭油味、顏色有焦黑色、深咖啡色皆屬劣質。

材　料：

乾珊瑚草 1 碗

（約 37.5 公克＝1 台兩）

小黃瓜 3 條

調味料：

檸檬 1 個

海鹽 1 茶匙

糖 1/2 茶匙

嫩薑絲半碗

紅辣椒絲 1/4 碗

好生之德本乎天　物物貪生樂自全
我要長年千歲祝　不教物命一朝延

————唐·白居易

46　開味妙品

雙椒豆干

（約 4~6 人份）

步　驟：
1. 豆干洗淨切絲。乾豆豉洗淨。青辣椒洗淨去籽，斜切 1 公分寬。
2. 油 1 大匙入炒鍋，待熱放入薑末炒香，加入豆豉炒香，加入豆干炒香，最後加入醬油、紅辣椒絲繼續炒至豆干熱透，即可起鍋。

秘　訣：　乾豆豉至少要洗 5 次以上，把外皮（表皮含有霉）洗掉效果佳。

知　識：　食肉者，通常被稱為「食物鏈」中最高的一環。依自然律，食物鏈中，大生物吃小生物，植物吃陽光、空氣和水，人類、動物吃植物或其他的動物。而今農夫在田裏施用殺蟲劑和化學肥料，動物吃了這些植物後，毒素留在牠們的體內。當我們人類吃了這些動物後，就將這些高濃度的毒素攝入體內，其含量有時高達植物含量的十倍以上。

材　料：
豆干 300 公克（半台斤）
乾豆豉半杯
青辣椒 100 公克（2.67 台兩）

調味料：
醬油 1 茶匙
薑末 1 茶匙
紅辣椒絲 1/2 茶匙

我認為素食者所產生性情上的改變和淨化，
對人類都有相當好的利益，所以素食對人類很吉祥。
—— 愛因斯坦(Albert Einstein)

  開味妙品

涼拌粉絲

（約 4~6 人份）

步　驟：
1. 冬粉洗淨汆燙撈起備用。將調味料全部加在一碗中調均勻備用。
2. 在食用前，將步驟 **1.** 加入紅蘿蔔絲、小黃瓜絲全部拌勻即可。

知　識： 早在三百多年前，山東招遠縣開始利用綠豆作原料製作粉絲。當時由於粉絲是由龍口港埠集中銷往世界各地，「龍口粉絲」由此而得名，外國人常譽粉絲為「中國玻璃絲、中國龍鬚、中國春雨」等美名。

材　料：
寬冬粉 2 把（洗濕後約 1.5 碗）
紅蘿蔔絲 1/4 碗
小黃瓜絲 1/2 碗

調味料：
薑絲 1/4 碗
醬油膏 1 大匙
糖 1/2 茶匙
醋 1 茶匙
香油少許

菩薩摩訶薩觀諸眾生，皆是親屬，乃至慈念如一子想，
是故不應食一切肉。

——《大乘入楞伽經》

開味妙品

懷鄉心葉

（約 4~6 人份）

步　驟：
1. 菜心葉洗淨，瀝乾水份，加入海鹽搓揉至軟，約醃一～二天，再洗一次，擠乾水份切細丁。素吉洗淨，切約 1 公分四方丁。
2. 油 1 大匙入炒鍋，放入素吉丁，炒至金黃色，加入醬油、菜心葉細丁，炒至乾香即可。

變　化：　可以用油菜、小芥菜、或芥藍做成這一道雷同的口味。視菜心葉的鹹度，再酌量加入調味料。

知　識：　在愛阿華州立大學所作的實驗中顯示：人體內的 DDT 大都從食肉中得來。他們也發現素食者體內 DDT 的含量不及肉食者的一半；在美國，據說人體內 DDT 量之高，就是食肉者也無法消受。
　　　　　但肉類中的毒素不只 DDT 而已，作為肉食用的動物常被餵以大量的化學飼料，及注射荷爾蒙等，使牠們迅速增肥長大，以改變體內的顏色、味道和纖維，這些添加物毒性很大。

材　料：
菜心葉 600 公克（1 台斤）
素吉 2 個

調味料：
海鹽
淡色醬油少許

眾生肉是好吃的，但我們為什麼不吃呢？
就因為我們要有慈悲心，要有愛護眾生的心。

—— 宣化上人

  開味妙品

味噌蘿蔔

步　驟：

1. 洗淨白蘿蔔晾乾（不用去皮），對切再對切（視蘿蔔大小而決定），再切約 3 公分正方（盡量使每一小塊都帶皮），加入海鹽略搓揉，用重物壓一天一夜（中途可再搓揉 2～3 次會比較柔軟、入味），取出放入布袋，再用重物壓一天或一夜，使水份流出。

2. 紅糖入炒鍋（不可有油漬）加一大匙水，用小火煮至香味溢出，加入味噌及一碗水煮滾起鍋，置涼備用。

3. 將步驟 1.加入步驟 2.拌均勻，分裝至乾燥玻璃瓶內，放入冰箱冷藏，醃漬三天後即可食用，並可保存一個月左右。

秘　訣： 用海鹽醃漬後，再用重物壓使水份流出，可以保存久一點。在製作過程不可沾到生水，否則易發霉。

變　化： 味噌可改用醬油 1 碗半、糖 500 公克、白醋 1 碗，同煮滾置涼後，加入蘿蔔同醃便是醬味蘿蔔。其餘作法同，並可保存更久，因醋有防腐之功能。

材　料：
白蘿蔔 6 公斤（10 台斤）

調味料：
海鹽 300 公克（8 台兩）
味噌 300 公克（8 台兩）
紅糖 1 碗

一切生物，佛皆視之如子，
救一物命，即是救佛一子，諸佛皆大歡喜。

—— 印光大師

食法譜界 開味妙品

黃芪酸梅

步　驟：

1. 買回來之黃芪再經過太陽晒乾一次（或用乾淨之鍋子以小火略烘焙乾燥）備用。並預先準備好乾淨、乾燥之玻璃罐。

2. 梅子（不用洗）直接加海鹽並拋翻數下後，用重物或石頭壓三天，再用其本身所釋出之水搓揉洗淨（即有消毒清洗作用，此時不可沾到水），瀝乾水份。

3. 步驟 2.之梅子加入砂糖並拋翻均勻，再用重物或石頭壓三天，利用其本身溶解之糖水搓揉清洗梅子，瀝乾水份（此時亦不可沾到水）。

4. 取出乾燥之玻璃罐，最底部先鋪一層步驟 1.之黃芪，再放入一層步驟 3.之梅子，再鋪上一層冰糖，至八分滿即可封罐。

5. 經過約兩個月，可在最上面一層加入冰糖（或視冰糖已溶解盡時，再加一層冰糖）。在六個月中，可加糖約 3 次，醃漬滿六個月後，即可取食。

秘　訣：　製作過程，不可用清水洗，以免發霉。黃色油質成份越高，代表黃芪等級越好。

材　料：

青梅 12 公斤（20 台斤）

海鹽 2 公斤（2 包）

砂糖 2 公斤（2 包）

冰糖 5 公斤（8.5 台斤）

黃芪 225 公克（6 台兩）

變　化：　黃芪也可改紫蘇，如果用鮮紫蘇，要晾乾水份再加入，以免發霉。亦可用乾品紫蘇（中藥房或青草店可買到），但風味不如鮮品佳。

知　識：　1. 梅子營養豐富，含蛋白質、脂肪、碳水化合物、多種有機酸和礦物質及對人體有益的 16 種胺基酸，味酸溫平，具有澄清血液、健胃強肝、消暑、生津、消除疲勞等保健功效。此外梅子亦有平氣安心，解除煩熱及消化不良之效。
　　　　　2. 紫蘇，性辛，溫。歸肺、脾經。營養豐富，有健胃、發汗、鎮咳去痰、利尿、淨血、鎮定作用，日本學者伊藤武認為紫蘇對疲勞、感冒、咳嗽、口腔炎、腦貧血、食欲不振、痢疾、精神不安均有療效，日本人普遍認為它能使人的神經系統得到休息。

輕

鬆 拈 來

Easy Buy   Easy Cook

Makes a Healthy and Easy Life

食材好買
配菜簡單
烹調容易
輕鬆享用
美味均衡
飲食加分

繞池閒走看魚遊　　正值兒童弄釣舟
一種愛魚心各異　　我來施食爾垂鈎

　　　　　　　　　　　　　　——唐·白居易

食法譜界　輕鬆拈來

香滷高麗

（約 4~6 人份）

步　驟： 1. 將高麗菜整顆洗淨，對切成 6 大塊。香菇洗淨泡軟，切絲。金針洗淨打結（或不打）。
2. 水入鍋（蓋過高麗菜的水量），大火煮滾，放入高麗菜、香菇、金針、醬油，先用大火煮滾後，改用小火燜 30 分鐘即成。

秘　訣： 購買頂端呈金字塔型的高麗菜比較甜。如果裝在保鮮盒，放進冰箱，可延長至一個月。

變　化： 用大白菜也可以滷出相當美味的菜餚。

知　識： 高麗菜含 A、C 等多種維他命。其含量超過桃、梨和蘋果，比西紅柿多三倍。高麗菜所含人體必需的微量元素，在各類蔬菜中名列前五名；其中鈣含量比黃瓜多四倍，比西紅柿多七倍。高麗菜含有較多的錳，可以促進物質代謝。所以，讓孩子多吃些高麗菜，對其發育成長大有益處。

材　料：
高麗菜 1 顆
香菇 6 朵
金針半碗

調味料：
醬油 3 大匙

至論護生一事，佛儒二教，若合符節。我佛以大慈大悲而為救世之本，
大慈者，與一切眾生之樂；大悲者，拔一切眾生之苦。

——圓瑛法師

輕鬆拈來

酪梨豆腐

（約 4 人份）

步　驟：　嫩豆腐，汆燙，撈起，待涼，切丁排入盤中。酪梨去皮去籽切丁，小心均勻放入嫩豆腐上。淋入醬油膏，最後洒上芝麻海苔鬆即成。

秘　訣：　用餐前才做較佳（或調味料食用前再洒上），因豆腐會生出水份，使得芝麻海苔變濕，會減少口感。

知　識：　酪梨富含植物性脂肪、蛋白質、胡蘿蔔素與維他命 B 群、C、E 及纖維、礦物質等，其脂肪為單元不飽和脂肪酸，能降低血中膽固醇量，預防心臟血管疾病，兼具抗氧化功能，有益於美膚養顏、防老化，在金氏世界紀錄中，其營養總評成績最高。

材　料：
酪梨半顆
嫩豆腐半塊

調味料：
芝麻海苔素鬆
1 大匙（一般超市可買）
醬油膏 1/2 茶匙

能夠茹素是最好的。但素食不要取什麼素雞、素鴨、素鱔魚等動物的名字，
單是起這些葷的名字，裏邊就含有染污的種子，所以以後不要用葷名去題素菜。

—— 宣化上人

輕鬆拈來

綠野四季

（約 4 人份）

步　驟： 四季豆去老絲洗淨，折段汆燙至熟透，撈起，瀝乾水份，加入海鹽、香油拌均勻，排入盤中，洒上黑芝麻即成。

秘　訣： 選擇四季豆時，以顏色嫩綠，豆身飽滿為嫩口；吃時，撕去莢筋，更覺滋味無窮。

變　化： 也可以用豇豆（長豆）或甜豆替代四季豆（敏豆）。

知　識： 四季豆能補血、明目、助排瀉、防腳氣。然而四季豆本身含有兩種毒素，分別為紅血球凝集素和皂素。它們對胃腸道有刺激性，可使人體紅血球發生凝集和溶血。這兩種毒素只要加熱至 100℃ 以上，就會被破壞。因此，調理四季豆必須將其全部煮熟燜透。

材　料：
四季豆 300 公克（半台斤）
熟黑芝麻少許

調味料：
海鹽 1/2 茶匙
香油少許

下功斷緣戒殺，中功斷緣兼素，上功斷緣放生。

——李炳南老居士

輕鬆拈來

香酥豆腐

（約 4 人份）

步　驟： 1. 水煮滾，豆腐放入汆燙，起鍋，瀝乾水份，待涼，切片狀，排入盤中備用。
2. 醬油、水 1/4 碗入鍋煮滾，起鍋淋入步驟 1.之豆腐上，洒上素香鬆、芹菜末即成。

秘　訣： 用餐前才做較佳（或調味料於食用前再洒上），因豆腐會生出水份，使得素香鬆變濕，會減少口感。

知　識： 豆腐的蛋白質含量比牛奶高一倍。豆腐是老年人補充蛋白質最佳來源，豆腐中的鈣、鎂、鐵含量較多，對骨骼、心臟和造血均有益。豆腐含有 8 種人體必需的胺基酸，還含有動物性食物缺乏的不飽和脂肪酸、卵磷脂等，可預防老年癡呆症。

材　料：
嫩豆腐 1 盒

調味料：
醬油 1/2 茶匙
素香鬆少許
芹菜末少許

諸餘罪中，殺業最重。諸功德中，放生第一。

——《大智度論》

輕鬆拈來

柔順干絲

（約 4~6 人份）

步　　驟：
1. 干絲入滾水中快速汆燙，撈起，瀝乾水份，備用。
2. 油 1 大匙入炒鍋待熱，放入薑片爆香，加入水半碗煮開，加入紅椒絲、青椒絲、海鹽待滾，最後加入干絲拌勻即可起鍋，淋上少許香油即成。

秘　　訣：
如果買回來的干絲是一般的（非軟的），在汆燙時可加入少許海鹽、白醋就可以變得比較柔軟。

變　　化：
也可以用小黃瓜絲替換青椒絲。

知　　識：
據傳，淮南王（漢高祖劉邦之孫）發明豆腐。到了宋代，已出現了「雪霞羹」、「東坡豆腐」、「蜜漬豆腐」、「啜菽」（五味拌豆腐條）等名菜。在清代，揚州廚師創製出了「加料干絲」。清人惺庵居士有一首《望江南》詞寫道：「揚州好，茶社客堪邀。加料干絲堆細縷，熟銅煙袋臥長苗，燒酒水晶肴」。這大約是有關干絲最早的詩詞了。

材　料：
軟干絲 300 公克（半台斤）
紅椒絲少許
青椒絲少許

調味料：
海鹽 1/2 茶匙
薑片 2 片
香油少許

世界所有的人不食眾生肉，而吃素、戒殺、放生，
如此世界災難就會消滅於無形。

—— 宣化上人

法界食譜 輕鬆拈來

芥末蒟蒻

（約 4~6 人份）

步　驟：
1. 蒟蒻洗淨，汆燙，撈起，直條對切排入盤中備用。
2. 沙拉醬加入芥末醬、海鹽、調均勻，淋入步驟 1.上面（或倒入拌勻）即可上桌。

秘　訣：　蒟蒻僅可冷藏，不可冷凍，否則質感變硬。

變　化：　也可將芥末醬加入少許醬油，口感亦不錯。或薑末、醬油膏、白醋、香油一起拌勻，淋入蒟蒻內即可食用。

知　識：　芥末含芥子成、芥子鹼、芥子酶、芥子酚以及脂肪、蛋白質、多種維他命等人體所必需的營養成分。本草記載「芥末辛熱無毒，具有散寒溫巾、通利五臟、健胃消食」等功效。但多食昏目動火，洩氣傷精。

材　料：
白蒟蒻條 600 公克（1 台斤）

調味料：
沙拉醬 2 大匙
芥末醬 1/2 茶匙
海鹽少許

没有什麼能夠比素食更能改善人的健康，
和增加人在地球上的生存機會了。

——愛因斯坦(Albert Einstein)

食法譜界　輕鬆拈來

雙色木耳

（約 4～6 人份）

步　驟： 1. 洗淨材料，去根部，用手撕成大小適中。
　　　　 2. 油 1 大匙入炒鍋，放入薑絲略炒，加入醬油，再炒
　　　　　　 出香味，放入雙色木耳，再翻炒，淋入半碗自熬高
　　　　　　 湯（或水），燜煮約 3 分鐘即可起鍋。

秘　訣： 黑木耳儘量用鮮品，其含鈣量較高，可常食用。

變　化： 也可以加些鳳梨片同炒，呈現別種風味。

知　識： 木耳含蛋白質、脂肪、糖和鈣、磷、鐵等礦物質，
　　　　　 以及胡蘿蔔素、核黃素、菸鹼酸等維他命。此外，
　　　　　 木耳中還含有對人體有益的植物膠質，這是一種天
　　　　　 然的滋補劑。木耳中所含的多醣體，可增加人體的
　　　　　 抗癌性。

材　料：
新鮮黑木耳 300 公克（半斤）
泡開白木耳 1 碗

調味料：
薑絲半碗
醬油 2 大匙

吃素幫助我成為一個全能運動選手，素食提供我額外的能量，
讓我能享受健康而充實的生活。
　　　　——莎莉・依斯德(Sally Eastall・歐洲金牌馬拉松選手)

輕鬆拈來

芝麻菠菜

(約 4~6 人份)

步　驟：
1. 洗淨菠菜，根部用刀刮乾淨，入開水汆燙，撈起用冷開水漂涼，瀝乾水份，切約 4 公分長段，排入盤內。
2. 醬油、糖、半碗水入鍋煮開，淋入步驟 1.之菠菜上，洒上芝麻即成。

秘　訣：
菠菜因含有草酸鹽，汆燙後再食用，對健康有益。

變　化：
也可以芥藍替換，或芝麻改成芝麻醬，有多種吃法。

知　識：
菠菜素有「蔬菜之王」之稱，含蛋白質（1 斤菠菜相當於 2 個雞蛋的蛋白質含量），維他命 A、維他命 B1、B2、C（為番茄的 3 倍）。其赤根中，含有一般蔬果所缺乏的維他命 K，有助於防治皮膚、內臟的出血。中醫認為菠菜性甘涼，利於清理人體腸胃的熱毒，能養血、止血、斂陰、潤燥。

菠菜切勿和豆腐一起食用，以免引起結石。

材　料：
菠菜 600 公克（1 台斤）
熟芝麻少許

調味料：
醬油 1 茶匙
糖 1/2 茶匙

一切諸肉，有無量緣，
菩薩於中，當生悲愍，不應啖食。——《大乘入楞伽經》

食譜法界　輕鬆拈來

甘味蒟蒻

（約 4~6 人份）

材　料：
蒟蒻 2 大塊

步　驟：
1. 蒟蒻洗淨切片，中間切一小刀，用一邊往中間穿過成花形條。
2. 湯鍋放水（蓋過材料）煮開，加入滷包、醬油、油、薑、及步驟 1.之蒟蒻，用小火煮約 15~20 分鐘，熄火燜約 10 分鐘使更入味，取用時淋上少許香油即可。

變　化：
蒟蒻不妨自己動手做（請參閱本書 22 頁），經濟實惠。

知　識：
蒟蒻的主要成分是葡萄糖及甘露糖鍵結的多醣類，屬水溶性纖維；由於人體中沒有酵素可以將其分解，也就不會被消化與吸收，能幫助腸胃蠕動，適度促進腸內廢物及有害菌之排泄，避免有害菌與腸道接觸的機會，可預防大腸癌的發生並具有整腸作用，所以也可以防止便秘。

調味料：
滷包 1 包
醬油 2 大匙
薑片 1 片
油 1 茶匙
香油少許

人人若能戒殺放生，
不吃一切肉類，則人的暴力思想就會消除。

　　　　　　　　　　　　——宣化上人

輕鬆拈來

蕨卷豆豉

(約 4~6 人份)

步　驟：　1. 蕨卷去老梗，洗淨切 4 公分長段。入沸水汆燙。
　　　　　2. 油入炒鍋，入豆豉、薑末炒香，入蕨卷，加入調味料略炒入味，即可起鍋上菜。

秘　訣：　蕨卷也可不汆燙直接炒，口感比較黏稠。

變　化：　起鍋前拌入碎花生，滋味香脆爽口，十分下飯。

知　識：　過溝菜蕨，閩南語稱為「過貓」，過溝菜蕨含有豐富的蛋白質、脂質、醣質、纖維質、鈣、磷、鐵、維生素 A 以及維生素 B 群。中醫認為過溝菜蕨性屬甘、寒、滑、無毒；對人體有清熱解毒、利尿、安神的功用。因此，過溝菜蕨被先民視為滋補的食物。

材　料：
蕨卷 600 公克（1 台斤）
濕豆豉 1/3 碗

調味料：
糖 1/2 茶匙
小辣椒 1 個
薑末 1/2 茶匙

浙江溫州，有一位姓蕭名震的人，當他小的時後，有一天突然夜夢一位金甲神，向他說：「孩子！你的壽命只能到十八歲。」蕭震醒來，惶惶不安，心中悽苦。他父親為官清廉，調陞到四川去，當時他以為自己不久於人世，不想隨父前去。但是他的父親一定要他隨侍在側。

到任後的第二天，四川主帥設宴為他父親洗塵，他也被邀前去。佳餚美酒，三巡之後，依照四川舊例要進玉箸羹一菜。

這玉箸羹的製法，極為慘忍，用火烙箸鑽母牛乳，乳出凝結於鐵箸之上，成為最佳上品餚饌。蕭震偶至廚房，見綁牛於木椿，便問廚師，廚師詳細告訴了他。蕭震大為驚愕，立刻奔到父親的面前，將所見所聞稟告父親，並請求說：「人為了口腹，以火箸凝乳，母牛定然痛苦萬分，請父親下命令，免去這種不人道的佳餚。」

他父親原極仁慈，立刻下令免去此種佳餚，生牛得救。過了幾日，又夢到那位金甲神，說道：「孩子！你積了陰德，不僅不會夭折，而且還可長壽，官至丞宰，希望你多多愛護生靈。」蕭震果然做丞宰，高壽至九十餘而死。

食法譜界　護生小故事

歡 樂 家 常

家常素菜超好吃
營養衛生都第一
老人孕婦及小孩
青年少年與壯年
呷呷舔唇味無窮
全家吃得樂開懷

少油無鹽羅漢齋　　供養臺灣眾英才
清淡品嚐波羅蜜　　同生極樂坐蓮臺

——宣化上人

歡樂家常

茭 白 仙 子

（約 4 人份）

步　驟：
1. 茭白筍去外殼洗淨切片（或塊）。黑木耳洗淨泡開，切片。紅甜椒洗淨切片。
2. 油入炒鍋待熱，入薑末炒香，加入茭白筍、黑木耳和一杯自製高湯（或水），燜煮約 3 分鐘，加入紅甜椒、調味料，略翻動並續煮約 1 分鐘即可起鍋。

變　化：　單單茭白筍清蒸，其味甜美。

知　識：　茭白筍在日本又稱「水燕麥」。中醫認為茭白筍性寒味甘，無毒。能解熱毒，除煩渴，利大、小便。治煩熱，消渴，黃疸，痢疾，目赤，風瘡。茭白筍因性寒，食用時，宜加辛溫佐料如薑等。茭白筍中含有草酸和難溶的草酸鈣，故患腎臟疾病及尿路結石者，不宜多食。

材　料：
茭白筍 4 隻
乾黑木耳 1 朵
紅甜椒半個

調味料：
海鹽 1/2 茶匙
薑末 1/2 茶匙
高湯 1 杯

如果要吃蛋的話，那也可以去吃肉。——宣化上人

竹笙絲瓜

（約 4 人份）

步　驟：
1. 絲瓜去皮洗淨，切 2 公分寬、3 公分長塊狀。竹笙洗淨泡開切段。枸杞洗淨備用。
2. 油入炒鍋待熱，放入薑末炒香，放入絲瓜略翻動，加入竹笙，蓋上鍋蓋，用中火燜煮約 3 分鐘，入調味料拌勻，起鍋洒上枸杞即成。

秘　訣：
絲瓜經過烹煮會生出大量水份，不用另外再加水，其本身水份就已足夠。

變　化：
起鍋前，加入少許九層塔，可變換另一種口感。

知　識：
選購竹笙時，應以其色澤淺黃、裙短肉厚、形狀均勻、質滑肉細、氣味清香（是自然香味，非人工加味）、無斷裂者為上品。買回來後，應放置在通風乾燥處，不能接觸陽光、不經過漂白。

材　料：
絲瓜 1 條
竹笙半碗（泡開）
枸杞 1 茶匙

調味料：
海鹽 1/2 茶匙
嫩薑末 1 大匙

一個只關心自己，卻視其他生靈毫無意義的人，
其生活不會健康快樂。

——愛因斯坦 (*Albert Einstein*)

歡樂家常

如 意 芽

（約 4~6 人份）

步　驟：
1. 洗淨所有材料備用。青江菜切約 4 公分長段，汆燙，漂涼備用。
2. 油 1 大匙入炒鍋，放入黃豆芽，翻炒，加入半碗水，用小火燜煮 5 分鐘，加入青江菜、紅蘿蔔片、海鹽、甘草水，翻炒 1 分鐘即可起鍋。

知　識：
1. 黃豆芽的外形似如意，亦稱為如意菜。戰國時期就有黃豆芽，稱為「黃卷」，那時主要做為藥用。黃豆芽不僅含有粗蛋白和胺基酸，也含有鈣、磷、鐵、鋅等礦物質及維他命，尤其維他命 C 的含量極高。
2. 青江菜含有各式營養素，每天食用能增加抵抗力，消除胃酸過多和便秘，阻擋膽固醇引起的動脈硬化。對於「清熱除煩，通利腸胃」更是效果特佳。中醫認為青江菜性平，味甘，通利腸胃、除胸中煩、消食下氣、治瘴氣、止熱氣嗽。

材　料：
黃豆芽 300 公克（半台斤）
青江菜 300 公克（半台斤）
紅蘿蔔片少許

調味料：
海鹽 1/2 茶匙
甘草水少許
（甘草半片泡水）

吾人當學佛之大慈大悲，實行戒殺放生，方是學佛之行。
是以學佛者，不僅持律戒殺，尤當竭力放生，方合我佛慈悲宗旨。
——圓瑛法師

菩提花生

(約 4~6 人份)

步　驟：
1. 花生洗淨，加一倍水，用大火煮開，改用小火燜煮至熟軟透。海帶洗淨剪成 1 公分寬。麵筋泡汆燙，瀝乾水份。
2. 將步驟 1.之所有材料入一鍋，加入醬油、水 3 碗，用小火燜煮至海帶軟即可。

知　識：
1. 將海帶置於放有乾燥劑的密封容器內，可做長期保存。海帶最怕濕氣，如果長出褐色粉末狀的霉時，就不能食用了。
2. 購買要炒或要煮的花生時，要選去外殼且表皮顏色比較清淡色、顆粒飽滿的，最好是當季收成的。並在要炒之前，再次的挑掉變色的或顆粒扁小的。

材　料：
花生 300 公克（半台斤）
海帶 1 條
麵筋泡半碗

調味料：
醬油 1 大匙

不殺為諸戒之首，而放生為眾善之先也。——諦閑法師

歡樂家常

高麗百燴

(約 4~6 人份)

步　驟： 1. 高麗菜洗淨，取出中心，整個入滾水，汆燙至整個熟透，撈起，瀝乾水份切成 5 大片，排入盤中備用。洋菇洗淨切薄片。洋芋、紅蘿蔔都去皮切細丁。毛豆洗淨。麵粉炒熟。

　　　　 2. 水 1 碗入炒鍋煮滾，放入洋芋丁、紅蘿蔔丁、毛豆煮熟，加入洋菇、玉米粒及少許油，再煮滾加入海鹽，熟麵粉調水，慢慢倒入鍋內，邊倒邊攪拌至均勻，起鍋前滴少許油，增加亮度，淋入步驟 1.之高麗菜上即可。

變　化： 玉米粒可改用玉米醬。

知　識： 中醫認為高麗菜味甘，性平、無毒。論其功能，《千金·食治》云：「久食大益腎，填髓腦，利五臟，調六腑。」《本草拾遺》亦云：「補骨髓，利五臟六腑，利關節，通經絡中結氣，明耳目，健人，少睡，益心力，壯筋骨。」不愧為強身壯體、健腦益智、延緩衰老之佳品。

材　料：
高麗菜半個
（約 600 公克＝1 台斤）
洋菇 1 碗
洋芋 1 個
紅蘿蔔 1/4 條
毛豆 1 大匙
玉米粒半罐

調味料：
海鹽 1/2 茶匙
麵粉 2 大匙

老農飯粟出躬耕　捫腹何殊享大烹
吳山四時皆是菜　一番過後一番生

　　　　　　　　　　　　——宋·陸遊

歡樂家常

芝麻牛蒡

(約 4~6 人份)

步　驟：
1. 牛蒡洗淨去皮，切絲（放入清水中浸泡，以免變色）。
2. 油 1 茶匙入炒鍋，放入牛蒡絲，加入醬油略炒，傾入水（材料的一半），用小火燜煮約 6 分鐘，入糖拌勻，再燜煮約 2 分鐘起鍋，灑上芝麻即可食用。

秘　訣：　牛蒡切絲後，立刻放入清水中浸泡，以免變色。

變　化：　可用四季豆替換牛蒡，有一點變化。

知　識：
1. 牛蒡含有高量粗纖維、菊醣、蛋白質、維他命 A、維他命 B1、菸鹼酸、維他命 C 及鉀、鐵、鈣、磷等礦物質。其中粗纖維可以刺激大腸蠕動、使排便順暢、幫助降低體內廢物囤積。
2. 購買牛蒡時，要選表皮飽滿、有重量，拿起來晃動時，有彈性感覺的為上品。

材　料：
牛蒡 1 條
熟芝麻 1 大匙

調味料：
醬油 2 大匙
糖 1 大匙

眾生惡殘暴　萬物樂仁慈
不嗜殺人者　遊山可跨獅

　　　　　　——弘一大師

  歡樂家常

番茄豆腐

(約 4～6 人份)

材　料：
板豆腐 1 塊
番茄 2 個
皇帝豆 4 兩

步　驟：
1. 板豆腐、番茄洗淨都切大丁。皇帝豆汆燙撈起，瀝乾水份。
2. 油入炒鍋，倒入番茄丁略炒香，加入所有的材料及調味料，加入 1 杯自製高湯（或清水），用小火燜煮約 5 分鐘（中途可開蓋輕輕翻動），徐徐倒入芡水拌勻（勾薄芡）即可起鍋。

秘　訣：皇帝豆料理前宜先泡水，烹飪後口感香甜鬆軟。

變　化：也可以比較單純不加皇帝豆的作法。

知　識：皇帝豆含有豐富的蛋白質、維他命和礦物質，它的含量雄居豆類作物之冠，1 公斤鮮豆含蛋白質相當於 2.36 公斤豬肉。所含胡蘿蔔素比胡蘿蔔高 4.4 倍。皇帝豆所含鐵、鈣、鋅、磷、鉀在農作物中是最高的，是補血、補鈣的好來源。皇帝豆雖然有利腸整胃作用，但食後易飽脹悶痛的人，卻不宜多吃。

調味料：
海鹽 1 茶匙
糖 1 茶匙

吃肉欲念多、妄想多，不容易得定；
不吃肉則少欲知足，沒有那麼多的妄想，因為氣血清而不混濁的緣故。

———宣
化上人

蒟蒻蘆筍

（約 4~6 人份）

步　驟：
1. 洗淨所有材料。蘆筍切 5 公分長段。將所有調味料加在一起，調均勻成醬汁備用。
2. 水入炒鍋待滾，把所有的材料逐一汆燙，用冷開水漂涼，瀝乾水份，排入盤中，沾醬料即可食用(或將醬料淋在上面)。

秘　訣：
這一道菜的做法非常簡單，只要汆燙食材後，再淋上醬料即可食用；又有多種顏色搭配，可謂是色香味俱全的佳餚。

變　化：
亦可用一般的蒟蒻，再切粗絲狀效果一樣好。

知　識：
綠筍的營養價值高於白筍，特別是維他命、鈣、鐵的含量遠高於白筍。蘆筍的性微溫、味苦、甘，可助消化，增食欲，提高機體免疫能力，排除體內自由基等有害物質，抑制癌細胞的活力。可克服人體疲勞症，對高血壓、動脈硬化、心臟病、肝炎、肝硬化、膀胱炎、腎炎、排尿困難、水腫等都有助益。

材　料：
玉米筍 1 碗
蘆筍 300 公克（半台斤）
蒟蒻絲小卷 1 碗
小番茄適量

調味料：
薑末 1/2 茶匙
白醋 1/2 茶匙
糖 1/4 茶匙
醬油膏 1 大匙
香油少許

夫食肉者，斷大慈悲佛性種子，一切眾生見而捨去。

——《佛說梵網經》

歡樂家常

雪 裡 春 曉

（約 4~6 人份）

步　驟：
1. 洗淨所有材料，瀝乾水份備用。雪裡紅切 1 公分細段。豆包切 1 公分正方細片，放入有油的炒鍋炒香後，加入醬油再炒香起鍋。毛豆汆燙撈起，入冷水漂涼，瀝乾水份。小辣椒切細丁。
2. 油 1 大匙入炒鍋，放入辣椒細丁略炒，加入雪裡紅略炒，再放糖、海鹽、及 2 大匙水，燜約 3 分鐘，加入步驟 1.之豆包、毛豆拌炒均勻即可起鍋。

秘　訣： 依雪裡紅鹹度，可增、減鹽量。

知　識： 綠色蔬菜（如青江菜、菠菜、空心菜等）於烹調時容易失去原有色澤。如要保持鮮綠原色，可在炒、煮時，同時加入小蘇打等鹼液，但鹼會破壞維他命群，如果不用鹼而改用海鹽，也有保持鮮綠效果，卻不會破壞營養分。

另一方法，將綠色蔬菜汆燙後，立即用冷水漂涼，亦可保持鮮綠之效果。

材　料：
雪裡紅 300 公克（半台斤）
豆包 3 片
毛豆半碗
小辣椒 1 個

調味料：
海鹽 1/4 茶匙
糖少許
醬油少許

一個國家偉大之處，
可由該國對待動物的方法中顯露無遺。

——甘地(Mohandas K Gandhi)

紅燒烤麩

（約 4~6 人份）

步　驟：
1. 烤麩掰開（或切）大小適中，入油鍋炸成金黃色（或煎成金黃色）。竹筍洗淨，去外殼，切滾刀狀備用。香菇洗淨泡開，擠乾水份，切片狀（或粗絲狀）。
2. 將步驟 1.之所有材料及調味料入炒鍋內，加入 2 杯自製高湯（或水），用小火燜煮約 8 分鐘，起鍋前淋上少許香油即成。

變　化：　烤麩也可以不經過油炸，直接煮，口感亦不錯，可節省烹調時間；而且不用擔心攝取的油量過高。

知　識：　香菇含有蛋白質、維他命 B 群、D1 及微量元素鋅和硒等礦物質。其十多種胺基酸中，其中有 7 種是人體必需的胺基酸。香菇中的香菇多醣、香菇嘌呤，可抗腫瘤、降膽固醇、抗血栓。中醫認為香菇性平味甘、治風破血、益胃助食。

材　料：
烤麩 5 個
竹筍 300 公克（半台斤）
香菇 3 朵

調味料：
醬油 1 茶匙
糖 1/2 匙
海鹽 1/4 茶匙
薑片 3 片

一切眾生皆有佛性，皆堪作佛。
我們如果殺了一個眾生，就等於殺一位佛一樣。

——宣化上人

歡樂家常

白果金針

（約 4~6 人份）

步　驟：
1. 洗淨所有材料。新鮮白果入滾水汆燙瀝乾水份。金針洗淨泡軟去老梗。新鮮木耳切大小適中備用。
2. 油 1 大匙入炒鍋待熱，放入淡色醬油略炒香，再加入白果、木耳、海鹽、糖、水 2 杯，用中火煮約 3 分鐘，最後加入金針再煮 2 分鐘即可起鍋。

知　識：
金針菜適宜氣血虧損，體質虛弱，心慌氣短之人食用；也適宜婦女產後體弱，月經不調者食用。然而新鮮金針菜中含有一類名為秋水仙鹼的物質，會氧化成有毒的二秋水仙鹼。所以金針菜千萬要煮熟、燒透， 除去毒素，方可食用。

材　料：

新鮮白果 1 杯（一般超市或傳統市場可買到）

乾金針 1 杯

新鮮木耳 1 杯

調味料：

海鹽 1/4 茶匙

糖 1/2 茶匙

淡色醬油 1/2 茶匙

希望社會諸君，勉力行之，即遇壽辰、結婚、生子，是自己求生，
慶生吉祥之事，均宜戒殺放生茹素，以善因而求善果也。

——圓瑛法師

糖醋金珀

（約 4~6 人份）

步　驟：
1. 素塊泡軟洗淨擠乾水份，加入醬油少許醃泡 30 分鐘，入油鍋炸成金黃色，起鍋備用。青椒洗淨去籽，切 2 公分小片。紅蘿蔔、洋芋去皮洗淨，切滾刀，入油鍋炸軟，起鍋備用。
2. 將所有調味料入鍋調均勻，用小火略煮，加入步驟 1.之所有材料拌均勻即可起鍋。

秘　訣： 綠色越濃、越有光澤的青椒越新鮮。不要挑表面有皺紋的，如果存放過久，就會從果蒂部分開始腐爛。

知　識： 青椒原產於南美洲，含有豐富的維他命 C、胡蘿蔔素，以及可防止維他命C氧化的維他命P，因此青椒中的維他命 C 不易被破壞。經常食用青椒，可改善肌膚粗糙、雀斑、黑斑、和消除疲勞、預防癌症、提升身體機能、抗老。

材　料：
素塊 1 碗
青椒 1 個
紅蘿蔔 1/4 條
洋芋 2 個

調味料：
海鹽 1/2 茶匙
糖少許
番茄醬 3 大匙
白醋少許
醬油少許

是亦眾生　與我體同　應起悲心　憐彼昏蒙
普勸世人　放生戒殺　不食其肉　乃謂愛物

———弘一大師

枸杞豆包

（約 4~6 人份）

步　驟： 1. 豆包入油鍋炸成金黃色，撈起瀝乾油份，切片，排
入盤內備用。香菇洗淨泡開，切片。豌豆仁汆燙，
瀝乾。枸杞洗淨備用。
2. 油 1 大匙入炒鍋待熱，放入香菇絲炒香，撈起備用。
再下薑末爆香，放入醬油、糖，加水 1 碗，煮開，
加入枸杞、香菇絲，續煮 2-3 分鐘，徐徐倒入芡水勾
薄芡，起鍋淋入步驟 1.之豆包上，洒上豌豆仁即成。

秘　訣： 煮芡汁時，要邊倒邊攪拌，否則會黏在一起不容易
散開。

變　化： 豆包也可以用豆條、或麵筋替換。

知　識： 枸杞具有促進和調節免疫功能、保肝、明目和抗衰
老三大作用。長期食用枸杞，可起強身健體、延緩
衰老、延年益壽之效。《本草彙言》記載：「常服
枸杞，氣可充、血可補、陽可生、陰可長、火可降，
風濕可去，有十全之妙用也。」

材　料：
厚豆包 4 片
豌豆仁 1 大匙
香菇 3 朵
枸杞 1 大匙

調味料：
醬油 3 大匙
糖 1 茶匙
薑末 2 大匙

飯疏（蔬）食飲水，曲肱而枕之，樂亦在其中；
不義而富且貴，於我如浮雲。

——《論語·述而》

美甘苦瓜

（約 4~6 人份）

步　驟：　1. 苦瓜對切，再切約 4 公分寬、5 公分長段，汆燙去苦味。梅乾菜洗淨切末。

　　　　　2. 將步驟 1. 之材料放入電鍋內鍋中，加入醬油、油及水 2 碗，略拌均勻。外鍋用 1 杯水，放入鍋內，蒸至電鍋跳起，不開蓋續燜 10 分鐘即成。

秘　訣：　汆燙可以減少苦味。

變　化：　也可以豆豉替換梅乾菜，口感亦不錯。

知　識：　苦瓜含有蛋白質、脂肪、維他命 B 群、維他命 C 及鐵、鈣、磷等礦物質。《本草綱目》稱苦瓜：「除邪熱，解勞乏，清心明目」，有潤膚、延緩衰老、明目的作用。

材　料：
白苦瓜 1 條
梅乾菜 8 分滿碗

調味料：
醬油 1 大匙
油 1 茶匙

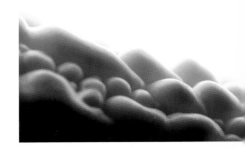

要想世界沒有災難，就要趕快戒殺、放生，
不吃眾生肉，以便挽回浩劫之來臨。

——宣化上人

丹汁豆腐

（約 4~6 人份）

步　驟： 1. 嫩豆腐切小丁。
2. 油 1 大匙入炒鍋待熱，放入紅蘿蔔泥略炒香，再放水 1 杯煮開，倒入豆腐丁、海鹽，用小火燜煮約 2 分鐘，徐徐倒入少許芡水拌勻（勾薄芡），輕輕略拌均勻，最後放入青豆仁，並淋上少許香油即可起鍋。

秘　訣： 豆腐是很容易破，煮的時候可以用有柄的鍋子，以手搖動的方式慢慢煮。

知　識： 豌豆，分軟莢及硬莢兩類。本省豌豆通常是指食用豆莢的軟莢種。而豌豆仁則是硬莢品種，它的莢殼粗硬不能用。豌豆仁富含維他命A、C、菸鹼酸、蛋白質、鈣質、鐵質、磷質等礦物質及其餘脂肪。其蛋白質的消化率比大豆蛋白質高；經常食用豌豆仁，可作為補充蛋白質的來源，且有利尿、清淨血液、防止孕婦口吐酸水之效。

材　料：
嫩豆腐 1 盒
紅蘿蔔泥 1 大匙
熟青豆仁 1/2 茶匙

調味料：
海鹽 1 茶匙
香油少許

何謂不殺生　內心無嫉瞋
忍即波羅蜜　一真一切真

——宣化上人

紅燒頁結

（約 4～6 人份）

步　驟：
1. 放入蓋過百頁結的水量，待水開，加入小蘇打粉 1/4 茶匙，放入百頁結，再待水開，撈起，漂涼。紅蘿蔔去皮洗淨，切滾刀。香菇泡軟，切大片。
2. 將步驟 1. 的材料放入電鍋內鍋中，加入醬油、油、海鹽、水 2 碗，略拌均勻。外鍋用 1 杯水，放入鍋內，蒸至電鍋跳起，即可取出食用。

秘　訣：
煮百頁結，水開時，要快速撈起，不宜煮太久，否則會過爛、或糊掉。

知　識：
黃色或橙黃色蔬菜（如胡蘿蔔、南瓜、番茄等）的顏色很少受烹調的影響。至於紅色蔬菜（如紅鳳菜、紅莧菜等）和白色或淡色蔬菜（如甘藍、白菜、蘿蔔、馬鈴薯等），如在烹調時加入少許醋，或其他酸性物質，可保持其鮮明的紅色和白色。

材　料：
百頁結 300 公克（半台斤）
紅蘿蔔 1 條
香菇 1/4 碗

調味料：
醬油 3 大匙
油 1 茶匙
海鹽 1/2 茶匙

少吃點肉類，可減少怪病。——宣化上人

食譜 法界 歡樂家常

青江香菇

（約 4~6 人份）

步　驟：
1. 青江菜洗淨備用。乾香菇泡軟，擠乾水份切絲。金針菇去根部，洗淨對切。紅蘿蔔去皮洗淨切絲。
2. 油 1 大匙入炒鍋，放入香菇絲、薑絲略炒香，放入紅蘿蔔絲、青江菜煮約 2 分鐘，再放海鹽，加入金針菇拌炒均勻，洒上少許香油，即可起鍋。

秘　訣： 青江菜亦可先經過汆燙，味道比較清香，但在汆燙過程，不必等水開，就要把菜撈起來入冷水，才能保持其鮮綠度。

變　化： 中式方面，青江菜除了清炒食用外，也可以當配菜，如做成上海菜飯、羹湯、炒飯等。用於西式，則可燙過馬上泡冰塊保持翠綠，要吃再燙一次，加入油、海鹽，使顏色更加亮麗。

知　識： 青江菜含有豐富的維他命 C 和鉀質，並且是鈣質的極佳來源，一杯份量的鈣質含量相當於 1/2 杯牛奶中的鈣含量。

材　料：
青江菜 600 公克（1 台斤）
乾香菇 3 朵
金針菇 1 把
紅蘿蔔 1/5 條

調味料：
薑絲 1 大匙
海鹽 1/2 茶匙
香油少許

好吃眾生肉，這裏頭都有一股冤業牽著，
令你歡喜犧牲其他生命，而來補助自己的生命。

——宣化上人

歡樂家常

翡翠珊瑚

（約 4 人份）

步　驟：
1. 山蘇洗淨去硬梗，切 3-4 公分小段。珊瑚菇洗淨，掰小塊，瀝乾水份備用。
2. 油 1 大匙入炒鍋，放入薑絲爆香，加入山蘇略炒，再加入醬樹子及汁、珊瑚菇、海鹽少許（先試試醬樹子之鹹度，再決定要加的海鹽量）、辣椒絲少許，略煮約 3 分鐘，滴入少許香油即可起鍋。

知　識：
珊瑚菇又名金頂蘑、榆黃蘑或玉皇蘑等。珊瑚菇具有滋補、強身的功效，可治療腎虛和痢疾。最近的研究發現，珊瑚菇具有抗腫瘤、抗疲勞、提高免疫力，及延緩衰老等作用。

材　料：
山蘇 225 公克（6 台兩）
珊瑚菇 150 公克（4 台兩）
醬樹子及汁半杯

調味料：
薑絲半杯
辣椒絲少許
海鹽少許
香油少許

啖肉者多病，當行大慈心，奉持不殺戒。

——《佛說十善戒經》

歡樂家常

禪悦高麗

（約 4~6 人份）

步　驟： 1. 洗淨所有材料。
2. 高麗菜切片。香菇洗淨泡軟，擠乾水份，和木耳皆切絲。番茄切片。芹菜切段。
3. 油 1 大匙入炒鍋，放入香菇炒香，加入高麗菜、紅蘿蔔絲、木耳絲、番茄、芹菜及水 1 碗，燜煮約 3 分鐘，加入海鹽拌勻即可起鍋。

秘　訣： 留住高麗菜營養，熱鍋快炒不過火。

知　識： 食物藉著消化之助而轉變成可溶解的汁液。因此我們吃蔬菜、果實及其他的鹼性食物，則體內對健康有益的鹼就會增加。除了使血液呈鹼性外，水果和蔬菜含有大量纖維質，粗糙的穀類，如糙米、全麥等，也都含有大量的纖維素。纖維素可以加快食物通過腸子的速度，因此可以促進消化，同時清理體內的組織。

材　料：
高麗菜半個
香菇 2 朵
鮮木耳 1 朵
紅蘿蔔絲少許
芹菜少許
紅番茄 1 個

調味料：
海鹽 1/2 茶匙

長生之道，宜早起，喜清靜，節制飲食。
若能遵守必可心中無欲、無怒，悠然過日，長壽人生由此可得。
　　　　　　　　　　　　　　　　　　　　——虛雲老和尚

三色飯糰

步　　驟：　取一乾淨耐熱塑膠袋（不要打開）鋪在下面，飯盛一半在塑膠袋上面，放入海苔醬抹平，再加上素鬆，然後把剩下來的飯全部蓋上，連同塑膠袋一起拿起捏緊，再將塑膠袋拉開包起來，立即食用或外帶皆可。

秘　　訣：　用熱米飯比較好捏。

變　　化：　飯糰的大小，可視自己之量決定。

知　　識：　黃豆、黃豆製品、及蔬菜水果中，皆含有異黃酮素，對更年期的女性而言是一大福音。它可以減少乳癌、攝護腺癌、減輕更年期的情緒不穩定。

材　　料：
飯 1 碗半
（白米、雜糧、黑糯米）
海苔醬 1/2 茶匙
芝麻海苔素鬆 2 大匙

浙江省湖州，有一窮苦人家，姓顏。

有一天，夫妻二人都出去幫人做工，只有一個五歲大的女孩子在家。這女孩在門前水池邊玩耍，不小心跌入池中，家裏所養的狗看到了，急忙跳入池中，把她救上岸來。但是小女孩已經喝了很多水，昏厥過去了。

狗又趕緊奔跑到顏某做工的地方，好像呼救的樣子！顏某一看，知道：「家中一定出了什麼事！」飛快地趕了回來。看見他的孩子伏在地上，只有點微弱的氣息了，急忙施行急救法，才將女孩救了過來。

溫馨靚湯

湯乃味之精　營養溶湯裏　日日都喝湯　身體真健康

世界是人心造成的，人心好殺，就是戰爭的世界；
人心好生，就是和平的世界。

——宣化上人

金銀涼心湯

（約 4~6 人份）

步　驟：　**1.** 所有材料洗淨。苦瓜去籽，切塊狀。玉米切小段。
金針去老梗（硬的部份），備用。

　　　　　2. 水入湯鍋待水滾，加入玉米段及苦瓜，用小火慢煮
約 30 分鐘，放入金針、海鹽，再煮 2 分鐘，即可起
鍋。

知　識：　　　金針菜所含的胡蘿蔔素量，竟超過胡蘿蔔的含量，
其他成份亦相當豐富，在蔬菜中可列入第一級。航
海船員常把它作為主要菜餚，用來代替素菜。中醫
認為，金針菜補氣血，強筋骨，利濕熱，寬胸膈。
並適宜心情抑鬱，氣悶不舒，神經衰弱，健忘失眠
之人食用。

材　料：

黃玉米 2 條
白苦瓜 1 條
金針（泡開）半碗

調味料：

海鹽 1/2 匙

人若能救助其他眾生，令他(牠)們離苦得樂，健康長壽；
自己也可以獲得同樣的果報。

——宣化上人

芹香茄湯

（約 4 人份）

步　驟：
1. 洗淨番茄，切薄片。
2. 水入鍋煮滾，放入紅番茄，用大火煮開，用小火煮 5 分鐘，加入芹菜絲、海鹽拌勻即成。

知　識： 芹菜的特點是株肥、脆嫩、渣少。芹菜含有較高的磷和鈣，常吃對高血壓、血管硬化、神經衰弱、小兒軟骨病等頗有助益。同時芹菜還含有揮發性的芹菜油，具香味，能促進食欲。中醫認為芹菜味辛、甘，性涼，清熱平肝，有健胃，降壓等功效。

材　料：
紅番茄 2 個
芹菜絲 1 大匙

調味料：
海鹽少許

蓮華蓮葉滿池塘　不惟花香水亦香
姊妹折時休折盡　留花幾朵護鴛鴦

——清・王淑

  溫馨靚湯

桂圓茴香

(約 4 人份)

步　驟：　1. 洗淨材料。茴香切 1 公分小段。
　　　　2. 水入鍋待滾，放入桂圓肉用小火熬煮約 15 分鐘。
　　　　3. 黑麻油入炒鍋，放入薑末略炒，加入茴香略炒，起鍋入步驟 2.內（或步驟 2.傾入），再煮約 5 分鐘即可起鍋。

知　識：　小茴香，有特異香氣，味微甜、辛。嫩葉可食用。子和葉都有順氣作用，用葉做菜餡或炒菜都可順氣健胃、散寒止痛，對生氣造成的胸腹脹滿、疼痛有較好效果。小茴香同時還有許多好聽的名字：蘹香、土茴香、野茴香、穀茴香、穀香、香子、小香。

材　料：
茴香 1 把
桂圓肉半碗

調味料：
薑末 1 大匙
黑麻油 1/2 茶匙

放生的意義，
是給面臨死亡威脅的眾生，一個活命的機會。

——宣化上人

食法譜界 溫馨靚湯

麻油豆包湯

（約 4~6 人份）

步　驟：
1. 豆包洗淨，擠乾水份，1 塊切成 4 小塊。
2. 黑麻油入鍋待熱，放入老薑末炒香，加入水約 4 碗待滾，加入豆包煮滾，改小火再煮約 5 分鐘即可。

變　化：
煮完後，加入傳統麵線（先用水洗後，再加入鍋中），即是麻油麵線。或不加豆包，只加麵線亦可。（喜愛更濃味時，亦可加少許當歸、枸杞同煮。）

知　識：
黑麻油可降低血壓，促進子宮收縮。據《本草綱目》記載：「黑麻油具補五內，益氣力，長肌肉、填髓腦、堅筋骨、明耳目、補肺氣、止心驚、利大小腸，輕身不老。」民間也認為有治白髮、養顏容、通潤便秘、淨化血液之效。

材　料：
豆包 300 公克（半台斤）

調味料：
黑麻油 1 大匙
老薑末 1 大匙

人若禁食哪一類眾生，即是度哪一類眾生。——宣化上人

溫馨靚湯

酸辣湯

（約 4~6 人份）

步　驟：
1. 金針菇去根部，對切洗淨備用。
2. 水入湯鍋，放入竹筍絲待滾，放入大白菜絲煮約 20 分鐘，加入腐皮絲續煮。
3. 油 1 大匙入炒鍋，放入醬油、香菇絲炒香，起鍋，加入步驟 2.的湯鍋內，再加入金針菇、烏醋、海鹽煮開，徐徐倒入茨水拌勻，洒些香油、胡椒粉即可起鍋。

知　識：
竹筍是一種低脂肪、高纖維、富蛋白質和醣類適量的保健食品，有寒士山珍之稱。科學研究發現筍尖可降血脂及肝脂質，筍底卻無此功能。而剛採收的新鮮竹筍，降血脂效果又優於置放多天再吃的筍子。

材　料：
大白菜絲 1 個
竹筍絲 2 大碗
香菇絲半碗
炸腐皮絲 1 碗
金針菇 2 把

調味料：
醬油 2 大匙
烏醋 2 大匙
胡椒粉適量
海鹽適量
香油適量

秋來霜露滿東園　蘆菔生兒芥有孫
我與何曾同一飽　不知何苦食雞豚

——宋・蘇軾

食法譜界　溫馨靚湯

玉米濃湯

（約 1~2 人份）

步　驟：
1. 馬鈴薯、紅蘿蔔去皮，洗淨切丁。麵粉用小火炒香，備用。
2. 水 4 碗入鍋煮開，放入馬鈴薯丁、紅蘿蔔丁，用小火煮至熟透，加入玉米粒、玉米醬、青豆仁煮滾。
3. 將炒香之麵粉加入半碗水調均勻，徐徐倒入鍋中，並邊倒邊拌勻，最後加入少許海鹽即可。

變　化：
麵粉可以一次多炒一點，放涼後，用密封罐保存，約可保存半個月至一個月。
（玉米粒、玉米醬本身已有甜味，亦可不加糖調味。）

知　識：
玉米脂肪中，含有 50% 以上的亞油酸、卵磷脂和維他命 E 等營養素，這些物質均具有降低膽固醇，防止高血壓、冠心病、細胞衰老，及腦功能退化等效果，亦有抗血管硬化的作用。要注意！玉米不宜久藏，否則易發黴，產生黃麴毒素；因此，買來後，最好盡速食用。

材　料：
馬鈴薯小 1 條
紅蘿蔔約 1/5 條
玉米粒半碗
玉米醬半碗
青豆仁少許
麵粉半碗

調味料：
海鹽少許
糖少許

夫乾曰大生，坤曰廣生，生物不息，天地之大德，
人秉天地之氣以生，當以天地好生之心為心。

——諦閑法師

溫馨靚湯

如意味噌湯

（約 4~6 人份）

步　驟：
1. 洗淨所有材料。豆腐切小丁。金針菇去根部，洗淨切段。味噌加入糖、水 1 大匙，調均勻備用。
2. 水入鍋待沸，放入黃豆芽，用小火煮 10 分鐘，加入豆腐、金針菇，再煮 5 分鐘，最後加入調均勻的味噌、海帶芽，再滾 1 分鐘即可起鍋。

變　化：
材料亦可只採用乾海帶芽、味噌及少許糖煮即可。
（若味噌本身甜度夠時，可不用另外再加糖調味。）

知　識：
春天是維他命 B2 缺乏症的多發季節，黃豆芽是含維他命 B2 較豐富的食品。春天，多吃些黃豆芽，可以有效地防治維他命 B2 缺乏症。烹調黃豆芽時，切不可加鹼，要加少量食醋，這樣才能保持維他命 B2 不減少。

材　料：
嫩豆腐 1 塊
乾海帶芽 1 茶匙
黃豆芽 300 公克（半台斤）
金針菇 1 把

調味料：
味噌 2 大匙
糖 1 茶匙

君子之於禽獸也，見其生，不忍見其死；
聞其聲，不忍食其肉，是以君子遠庖廚也。

——孟子

簡易藥膳

（約 4 人份）

步　驟： 取一盅或陶瓷大碗，放入四物、麵筋糰、開水，入蒸鍋，用中火蒸約 50～60 分鐘（或用電鍋蒸）即可食用。

變　化： 也可以四神、或八珍替換。

知　識： 生地、熟地，均來源於玄參科植物——地黃的乾燥根。生地，為鮮品的乾燥品；熟地，為生地的蒸製品。

熟地長於補血、滋陰生津、補精益髓，還有益於精血虧虛的腰酸、腳軟、頭昏眼花、耳聾耳鳴、鬚髮早白等症。可是，熟地性滋膩，不甚易消化。

材　料：
加味四物一包
（當歸 川芎 白芍 熟地 紅棗 枸杞 黃芪）
自製炸麵筋糰 3 個
（見本書 20 頁）

調味料：
海鹽少許（亦可不加）

關中有一商人到隴山做生意，偶然得到一隻會說話的鸚鵡，商人十分喜愛，飼養很慇懃。

後來商人偶因小事入獄，幾天後，才被釋放。回到家裏非常憤恨，時常唉聲歎氣！鸚鵡對他說：「你被關了幾天，就受不了，而我一直被關著好幾年，叫我怎麼能受得了？」商人聽了很慚愧！就立刻放牠回隴山。

後來商人的朋友，有經過隴山的，鸚鵡一定在樹上對他說：「我的主人身體平安嗎？請代我向他問候！請代我向他問候！」

香噴噴呀熱呼呼　西里呼嚕真好吃　有湯有菜還有麵　省時美味又方便

麵面俱到

我們學佛的人，第一要沒脾氣，第二要不殺生。

——宣化上人

麵面俱到

無心茄汁麵

（約 2 人份）

步　驟：
1. 通心麵入滾水煮熟，撈起，瀝乾水份備用。番茄洗淨切大丁。四季豆去老絲切小段汆燙，入冷開水漂涼備用。洋菇洗淨切大丁備用。
2. 油 1 大匙入炒鍋，放入番茄略炒，加入淡色醬油少許再炒後，入洋菇、海鹽、糖，略翻動，用小火燜煮約 5 分鐘，加入通心麵翻炒均勻起鍋，洒上四季豆即可。

變　化： 通心麵也可以用意大利麵替換。也可以將步驟 2.之材料加入，蓋過材料的水，用大火煮滾，小火燜煮即成番茄湯，加入麵即是番茄湯麵，口感很不錯，不妨試試。

知　識： 番茄最主要的營養價值在於茄紅素及維他命C，茄紅素具有預防心血管疾病，與抑制攝護腺癌的效果；番茄不同於其他蔬菜水果的地方，在於番茄必須要加熱後才能破壞其纖維結構，使其中的茄紅素得以釋出，為人體吸收。所以煮熟的番茄，其茄紅素遠優於新鮮的番茄。

材　料：
通心麵 1 碗
番茄 2 個
四季豆半碗
洋菇約 5 朵

調味料：
海鹽 1/2 茶匙
糖 1/2 茶匙
淡色醬油少許

古聖先賢，莫不以仁慈濟物，博愛利生；
是知凡屬人者，要當以存仁心。

——諦閑法師

  麵面俱到

祥瑞米粉

(4~6 人份)

步　驟： 1. 洗淨所有材料。高麗菜切絲。
2. 油 2 大匙入炒鍋，待熱，放入香菇絲炒香，加入醬油再炒香，加入高麗菜絲、紅蘿蔔絲、炸豆包絲，翻炒至高麗菜軟，加入自製高湯（請參照本書 16.17 頁）（或水）3 碗、海鹽、糖、胡椒粉，待滾。
3. 放入米粉、綠豆芽，改用小火，同時用筷子翻炒米粉，直到和其他材料拌均勻及無湯汁，再洒入芹菜末拌勻即可起鍋。

秘　訣： 米粉炒好後，味道若不夠鹹時，可再加些海鹽調味。此時若再加醬油，會有酸酸的口感。若較喜歡醬油口味，可在炒香時加多一點。

變　化： 米粉換成麵條即是炒麵。

知　識： 五胡亂華，中原人南遷閩、浙、贛時，以稻米榨條而食（即現在的米粉。）早期民間，將米粉視為高級食品，只有貴客光臨或年節喜慶的時候，才可以看到炒米粉上桌。日據時期與光復後早期，約八斤白米只能換五斤米粉；在一支番薯籤扛三粒米的時代，白米已算珍貴了，米粉更是不在話下。

材　料：
米粉 1 包
高麗菜半個
綠豆芽 300 公克（半台斤）
紅蘿蔔絲 1/4 碗
香菇絲半碗
炸豆包絲 1 碗

調味料：
醬油 2 大匙
海鹽 1 大匙
糖 1/2 茶匙
胡椒粉 1/4 茶匙
芹菜末半碗

君心仁慈禪悅為食　康泰平安法喜充滿

——宣化上人

麵面俱到

君康麵線

（約 4～6 人份）

步　驟：
1. 將枸杞、桂圓肉、老薑末、玉桂粉、當歸、黑麻油、醬油等放入鍋內，加入半鍋水（10 人份電鍋），用小火燜煮 40 分鐘，熄火備用。

2. 水入鍋燒開，將麵線下鍋煮熟，撈入盤內，淋上步驟 1.之食料後即可享用。

秘　訣：　適用於較寒性體質者，或長素者。

知　識：　從南北朝開始，當歸就被視為補血、活血珍品。當歸可調整生理機能、補血調經、活血止痛、澤顏潤膚、生肌強體、滋補強身、延年益壽。科學試驗證明，當歸還能增加冠狀動脈血流量，降低耗氧量，從而改善心臟功能。當歸還有鎮靜、鎮痛、抗炎作用。

材　料：
傳統長麵線 2 把
枸杞半碗
桂圓肉半碗

調味料：
老薑末半碗
玉桂粉 1/2 茶匙
當歸 1 片
黑麻油 2 大匙
醬油 1 大匙

已赴網羅遭困厄　將投湯火受驚忡
臨刑遇救恩無極　彼壽隆兮爾壽隆

——壽光禪師

食法譜界　麵面俱到

清香湯麵

(約 4 人份)

步　驟： 1. 金針洗淨去老梗。炸豆包切絲。竹筍去外殼老皮，切細絲。豆干洗淨切絲。清江菜洗淨備用。
2. 水入鍋放入竹筍煮滾，再用小火煮約 10 分鐘，加入金針、炸豆包絲、豆干絲再煮滾，加入所有的調味料，煮滾即成清香湯，備用。
3. 另一鍋水待滾，放入麵條煮至浮起，加入清江菜待滾，撈入步驟 2.內，淋入少許香油即成。

秘　訣： 麵另外煮熟再加入湯汁內，是讓湯喝起來爽口。

變　化： 也可以將生麵條加在步驟 2.內直接煮熟，再加入清江菜，不過湯汁比較濃稠。

知　識： 綠葉的蔬菜，極富人體不可或缺的多種維他命與礦物質，並有淨化血液的功能，中國醫藥學會建議，每天最好吃 500 公克的綠葉蔬菜。

材　料：
麵條 4 人份
金針 20 朵
炸豆包 4 片
竹筍 300 公克（半台斤）
五香豆干 3 片
清江菜 300 公克（半台斤）

調味料：
醬油 1 茶匙
海鹽 1/2 茶匙
糖 1/2 茶匙

口腹貪饕豈有窮　咽喉一過總成空
何如惜福留餘地　養得清虛樂在中

———宋·蘇軾

食法譜界 麵面俱到

健康三明治

(1~2 人份)

步　驟：
1. 油 1 茶匙入炒鍋，放入豆包，煎成兩面金黃色即可起鍋。
2. 吐司抹上沙拉醬，依序放入生菜片、豆包、番茄片，最後蓋上已塗抹沙拉醬之吐司即可食用。

變　化：　亦可以酪梨替代豆包，或以小黃瓜片替換生菜。

知　識：　生食有許多的好處——維他命不被破壞，生鮮蔬菜如單獨食用，有利營養吸收。食後約 30 分鐘，胃即排空，可減輕胃腸負荷，對健康有益。生食的條件就是蔬菜、水果及芽菜等，一定要清潔。而，台灣農藥的使用，年年成長，殘毒問題嚴重，故而生食必須注意仔細洗滌蔬果，方能達到生食的效果。

材　料：
全麥吐司 4 片
生菜 2 片
番茄 4 片
豆包 2 片

調味料：
無蛋沙拉醬 2 茶匙

「天行健，君子以自強不息……」，人的生活起居順應著天體的循環，方能達到天人合一的理想 。

《黃帝內經》中說：「智者之生也，必須順四時而避寒暑。」「因時養生」是養生的一條重要原則，人體必須順應四時自然變化而養生，從而加強人體適應季節與氣候變化的能力，以保證身體健康，減少疾病的發生。

一年四季，春溫，夏熱，秋涼，冬寒。氣候的變化，會給人體帶來不同程度的影響。因此，機體的營養結構要隨季節的變化予以協調，注意各個季節的飲食方式。春季宜食清淡；夏季宜食甘涼；秋季燥熱，宜食生津食品；冬季寒冷，宜食溫熱。在飲食順應四時，可保養體內陰陽氣血，使正氣在內，邪不可發。

四季養生概念

春天養生

萬物生長始於春季，天氣由寒轉溫，草木萌芽，萬物復蘇。五行學說中，肝屬木，與春相應，主升發，體內以肝、膽經脈的經氣最旺盛和活躍。此時要注意肝臟的保養，肝性喜暢達疏泄而惡抑鬱，所以務使精神愉快，養肝首要一條是調理情志。不良的情緒易導致肝氣鬱滯不暢，使神經內分泌系統功能紊亂，免疫功能下降，容易引發精神病、肝病、心腦血管病、感染性疾病。因此，春天應注意情志養生，保持樂觀開朗的情緒，以使肝氣順達，起到防病保健的作用。

《黃帝內經·素問》寫道「春三月，此謂發陳，天地俱生，萬物以榮，夜臥早起，廣步於庭，披髮緩形，以使志生，生而勿殺，予而勿奪，賞而勿罰，此春氣之應，養生之道也，逆之則傷肝，夏為寒變，春長者少。」這是說，人們在春季裏應該早起，在院子裏多散步，以發佈「生」氣，舉止要和緩輕柔以應春氣，並且使身心保持舒暢、活潑，以適應春生之氣，切記惱怒、殺奪、刑罰之念頭，從而使肝氣保持正常的升發和調暢，如果違背了這一個自然規律，就會損傷肝氣，到了夏天容易罹患寒性的疾病，使人體適應環境的能力減低了，這便是春季養生的大原則了。

早春時節，氣溫仍較寒冷，孩童、老人和身體虛弱的人，應隨時保暖，以免外感，平時也可煮些橘子皮、金桔、蘿蔔、梨子或荸薺當茶喝。人體為了禦寒，要消耗一定的能量來維持基礎體溫，所以早春期間的營養構成應以高熱量為主，除穀類製品外，還應選用黃豆、芝麻、花生、核桃等食物，以便及時補充能量物質。春天氣溫變化較大，細菌、病毒等微生物開始繁殖，活力增強，容易侵犯人體而致病，所以，在飲食上應攝取足夠的維他命和無機海鹽。小白菜、油菜、甜椒、番茄等新鮮蔬菜和柑橘、檸檬等水果，富含維他命C，具有抗病毒作用：胡蘿蔔、莧菜等黃綠色蔬菜，富含維他命A，具有保護和增強上呼吸道粘膜，和呼吸器官上皮細胞的功能，從而可抵抗各種致病因素侵襲：富含維他命E的食物也應食用，以提高人體免疫功能，增強機體的抗病能力，這類食物有芝麻、高麗菜、花椰菜等。

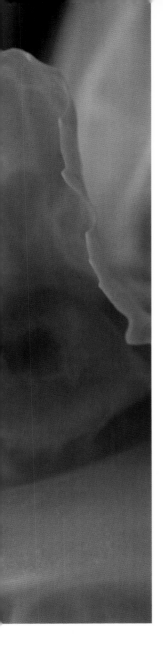

中醫還認為：「春日宜省酸增甘，以養脾氣。」這是因為春季為肝氣旺之時，肝氣旺則會影響到脾，所以春季容易出現脾胃虛弱病症；而多吃酸味的食物，會使肝功能偏亢，所以春季飲食調養，宜選辛、甘溫之品，忌酸澀。飲食宜清淡可口，忌油膩、生冷、粘硬及刺激性食物。要多食，如黃豆芽、綠豆芽、豆腐、豆豉、大麥、小麥、大棗、花生、黑芝麻、柑桔、薑、香菜之類的食材；由於冬季新鮮蔬菜較少，攝入維他命不足，聚積一冬的內熱要散發出去，所以還要多吃些新鮮蔬菜，如蘆筍、油菜、菠菜、芹菜、薺菜、枸杞、香椿等。這對於因冬季過食膏粱厚味導致內熱偏勝者，還可起到清熱瀉火、涼血明目、消腫利尿、增進食欲等作用。

夏季 養生

夏季炎熱，多雨高溫，出汗過多易耗傷氣陰，應補氣養陰，清熱祛濕防暑，出汗多時，還應注意飲些海鹽水；內衣內褲應勤洗勤換。久病臥床的病人要經常用溫水洗澡，常換貼身衣被，以防褥瘡和痱子等皮膚病的發生。

夏季氣溫高，人體神經經常處於緊張狀態，某些分泌腺的功能也受影響，因而常出現消化力減弱、食欲不振現象，故應適當多吃些清淡而易消化的食物，如豆製品、新鮮蔬菜、瓜果等，少吃油膩食物。夏季人體水分和海鹽丟失較多，應多喝水，並適量飲些淡海鹽水。但切忌飲水過多，以免增加心臟和消化系統的負擔，應採取少量飲的方法。

夏季要多吃瓜類蔬菜。蔬菜中的水分是經過多層生物膜過濾的天然、潔淨、營養且具有生物活性的水，是任何飲用水所無法比擬和替代的。夏季也正是涼性蔬果上市旺季，它們的共同特點是含水量都在 90％以上。冬瓜含水量居眾菜之冠，高達96％，其次是黃瓜、金瓜、絲瓜、佛手瓜、南瓜、苦瓜、西瓜等。番茄、茄子、芹菜、生菜、蘆筍、豆瓣菜、涼薯等也屬於涼性蔬菜，不妨經常食用。夏季如經常喝綠豆湯、菊花茶、冬瓜茶、蓮藕茶等，既能防暑清熱，又能解毒開胃。但是忌貪冷飲，免傷脾胃。

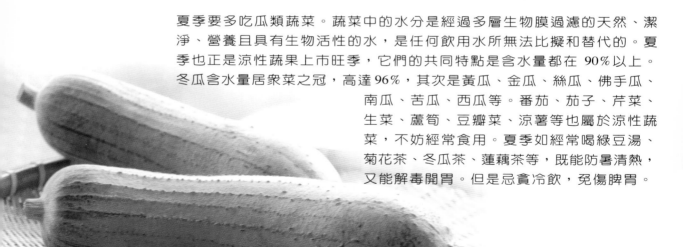

秋季 養生

時至秋令，碧空如洗，地氣清肅，金風送爽，萬物成熟，正是收穫的季節。秋季的氣候是處於「陽消陰長」的過渡階段，立秋至處暑，秋陽肆虐，溫度較高，加之時有陰雨綿綿，濕氣較重，天氣以濕熱並重為特點，故有「秋老虎」之說。

「白露」過後，雨水漸少，天氣乾燥，晝熱夜涼，氣候寒熱多變，稍有不慎，容易傷風感冒，許多舊病也易復發，被稱為「多事之秋」。

由於人體的生理活動與自然環境變化相適應，體內陰陽雙方也隨之發生改變。因此，秋季養生在對精神情志、飲食起居、運動導引等方面進行調攝時，應注重一個「和」字。我國自古以來流傳的「春捂秋凍，不生雜病」的諺語，符合秋天「薄衣禦寒」的養生之道。但對「秋凍」要有正確的理解，領悟其中真髓。

自「立秋」節氣以後，氣溫日趨下降，晝夜溫差逐漸增大，寒露過後，北方冷空氣會不斷入侵，出現「一場秋雨一場寒」。從防病保健的角度出發，循序漸進地練習「秋凍」，加強禦寒鍛煉，可增強心肺功能，提高機體適應自然氣候變化的抗寒能力，有利於預防呼吸道感染性疾病的發生。

如果到了深秋時節，遇天氣驟變，氣溫明顯下降，陰雨霏霏，仍是薄衣單褲，極易受到寒冷的刺激，導致機體免疫力下降，引發感冒等病，特別是患有慢性支氣管炎、哮喘、慢阻肺、心腦血管病、糖尿病等病的中老年人，若不注意天氣變化，防寒保暖，一旦受涼感冒，極易導致舊病復發。寒冷刺激可致體表血管彈性降低，周圍阻力增加，使交感神經興奮，腎上腺皮質激素分泌增加而引起小動脈收縮、血壓升高，易發生腦血管破裂出血。寒冷刺激還能使血液纖維蛋白濃度上升，血液黏稠度增加，導致血栓形成，危及生命和健康。

因此，要順應秋天的氣候變化，適時地增減衣服，做到「秋凍」有節，與氣候變化相和諧，方為明智之舉。

156

秋天氣壓較高，溫度減低，而且空氣乾燥，因此秋天要防燥養陰，其養生離不開潤燥、暖體、養肺、益氣。

在飲食方面，秋天要多吃些滋陰潤燥的食物，避免燥邪傷害。少攝取辛辣、多增加酸性食物，以加強肝臟功能，因為中醫認為「肺氣太盛可剋肝木，故多酸以強肝木。」從食物屬性解釋，少吃辛，以免加重燥氣。

多吃酸食有助生津止渴，但也不能過量。酸性食物諸如：芝麻、核桃仁、銀耳、菠菜、茄子、四神等，多吃山楂、豆腐、蘋果、葡萄、石榴、楊桃、檸檬、柚子、柿、柑桔、梨、葡萄和龍眼等，要少食辣椒等耗氣辛辣之品。秋天要少吃生菜沙拉等涼性食物，食物最好過個火，燙一燙再吃。就太陽能量來說，秋天陽氣漸收，陰氣慢慢增加，不適合吃太多陰寒食物。尤其應避免瓜果，因為秋瓜壞肚，像是西瓜、香瓜易損脾胃陽氣。

《黃帝內經·素問》指出：「秋涼冬寒，陽氣漸衰。」冬天人體內腎和膀胱經脈的氣旺，冬季養生基本的原則仍然是《黃帝內經》中的一句格言：「春夏養陽，秋冬養陰。」冬天萬物斂藏，我們（尤其是老年人）養生就該順應自然界收藏之勢，收藏陰精，使精氣內聚，以潤五臟。用藥則以滋陰藥來補益陰氣，衣著則不必過厚過暖等等。而以上原則主要是從強化腎的功能著手的。所以，一切有關補益腎臟、強化腎臟、養護腎臟的養生方法，也就是中老年人冬季養生的主要內容和第一選擇。

冬季 養生

從中醫角度來看，腎是人體生命之源。腎中的精（氣）為機體生命活動之本，腎關係人的生長，發育與衰老，老年人往往都有腎虛徵象。久病之人也常見腎虛，即所謂的「久病窮必及腎」。李時珍說：「生薑之辛補肝，炒海鹽之鹹補心，甘草之甘補脾，五味子之酸補肺，黃柏之苦補腎。又如茯神之補心氣，生地黃補心血；人參之補脾氣，白芍藥之補脾血；黃芪之補肺氣，杜仲之補腎氣，熟地黃之補腎血；川芎之補肝氣，當歸之補肝血。（以上）皆為補劑，不特人參為補也。」由此可知，用鹽黃柏、炒杜仲、熟地三味來進補，是冬季補腎的正統。這也是順冬沈之氣，冬日進補宜加苦寒藥，順時令氣節以養性延命的「天人相應」理論的體現。

冬季自然界陰氣最盛，陽氣最弱，陰長陽消達到頂點。人體遭受寒氣冷風侵襲，寒邪最易入腎而引起多種疾患，這時要注重溫腎抑陰護陽，以提高抗禦風寒的能力。就飲食而言，凡性溫或有補腎作用的食物，均在首選之列。雜糧類：如糯米、高粱、黍米、燕麥；蔬菜類：如辣椒、大頭菜、香菜、生薑；果品類：如桂圓、荔枝、紅棗、山楂、核桃、栗子等。多吃這類食物，就在於它們均為性溫，多為冬令滋補良品，且驅散寒冷，溫腎而增加體熱。

五色之一的黑，於五行中屬水，走腎經，如黑米、黑豆、黑芝麻、黑棗、黑木耳、海帶、紫菜等，多吃這類，食物有明顯補腎作用。而，黃色蔬菜如胡蘿蔔、黃花菜、花生、山藥、南瓜之類，所含成份以黃酮類為主，在生理上可減低血管滲透和防止血管破裂。血管遇嚴寒易收縮硬化破裂，甚至有釀成腦溢血的危險，故此時應多吃黃色蔬菜。

此外，冬季固然寒冷，但人們穿衣多、住房暖、活動少，飲食所含熱量偏高，體內容易積熱，故冬季也會時有肺火顯盛的現象。對此，不妨再適當吃一點屬性偏涼的食物，如白蘿蔔、大白菜、芹菜、菠菜、冬筍、香蕉、生梨、蘋果。這樣，既能補不足，又可清有餘。

冬季 養生

除上述養生法之外，飲食調養尚有三宜：

一.宜粥糜，古代養生家多提倡深冬晨起宜喝些熱粥。《飲膳正要》中認為冬季若在粳米粥中加點紅棗、紅豆可使人覺周身溫暖，精力倍增。民間有冬至吃紅豆粥，臘月初八吃「臘八粥」，臘月二十五吃「八寶粥（飯）」的習慣。冬日宜食養心除煩的麥片粥，消食化痰的蘿蔔粥、補肺益胃的山藥粥，養陰固精的核桃粥，健脾養胃的茯苓粥，益氣養陰的大棗粥，調中開胃的玉米粥，滋補肝腎的紅薯粥等。

二.宜溫熱之品，以取陽生陰長之義。如宜吃桂圓肉、棗、山藥、糯米等。體肥者忌肥甘溫熱厚味。

三.宜堅果，冬日多吃點核桃、板栗、松子、花生、葵花子、芝麻、黑豆、黑米等。俗語說：「三九補一冬，來年無病痛。」冬季適當進補，可提高機體的抗病能力。此時，人的皮膚緻密，出汗較少，攝入的營養物質也容易貯藏起來，為明年開春乃至全年的健康打下良好的基礎。

因為溫室效應的日趨嚴重，台灣的四季越來越不明顯了，但是飲食養生的方法卻是一樣的，要針對氣候與自身的情況來調整飲食：不論吃什麼、補什麼，都不可毫無節制，千萬不要將食補吃成食傷。也不要吃昂貴或進口的蔬果，因為越昂貴的蔬果越是可能不對季，進口的蔬果也常都經過防腐的處理。也盡量不要吃一些精製的食物，因為越精製的食物離健康越遠，當然也離修行更遠了。順著季節吃當季盛產的食材，就最容易與自然相應了。俗云：「布衣暖，菜根香，讀書滋味長。」希望大家讀了這本食譜，能更深體會菜根之香與滋味之長。

祖師的叮嚀

——蓮池大師戒殺放生文

蓮池

大師戒殺放生文

世人食肉，咸稱理所當然；乃恣意殺生，廣積怨業；相習成俗，不自覺知。
昔人有言：「可為痛哭流涕長太息者」是也。
計其迷執，略有七條；開列如左，餘可例推云。

一曰、生日不宜殺生

「哀哀父母，生我劬勞。」己身始誕之辰，乃父母垂亡之日也。是日也，正宜戒殺持齋，廣行善事；庶使先亡考妣，早獲超昇；現在椿萱，增延福壽。何得頓忘母難，殺害生靈，上貽累於親，下不利於己？此舉世習行而不覺其非，可為痛哭流涕長太息者，一也！

二曰、生子不宜殺生

凡人無子則悲，有子則喜；不思一切禽畜，亦各愛其子。慶我子生，令他子死，於心安乎？夫嬰孩始生，不為積福，而反殺生造業，亦太愚矣！此舉世習行而不覺其非，可為痛哭流涕長太息者，二也！

三曰、祭先不宜殺生

亡者忌辰，及春秋祭掃，俱當戒殺以資冥；殺生以祭，徒增業耳！夫八珍羅於前，安能起九泉之遺骨而使之食乎？無益有害，智者不為矣。此舉世習行而不覺其非，可為痛哭流涕長太息者，三也！

四曰、婚禮不宜殺生

世間婚禮，自問名納采，以至成婚，殺生不知其幾？夫婚者，生人之始也；生之始而行殺，理既逆矣。又婚禮，吉禮也；吉日而用兇事，不亦慘乎？此舉世習行而不覺其非，可為痛哭流涕長太息者，四也！

五曰、宴客不宜殺生

良辰美景，賢主佳賓，疏食菜羹，不妨清致。何須廣殺生命，窮極肥甘；笙歌鼎飲於杯盤，宰割怨號於砧几？嗟乎！有人心者，能不悲乎？此舉世習行而不覺其非，可為痛哭流涕長太息者，五也！

六曰、祈禳不宜殺生

世人有疾，殺生祀神以祈福佑。不思己之祀神，欲免死而求生也；殺他命而延我命，逆天悖理，莫甚於此矣！夫正直者為神，神其有私乎？命不可延，而殺業具在。種種淫祀，亦復類是。此舉世習行而不覺其非，可為痛哭流涕長太息者，六也！

七曰、營生不宜殺生

世人為衣食故，或畋獵，或漁捕，或屠宰牛羊豬犬等，以資生計。而我觀不作此業者，亦衣亦食，未必其凍餒而死也。殺生營生，神理所殛；以殺昌裕，百無一人。種地獄之深因，受來生之惡報，莫斯為甚矣！何苦而不別求生計乎？此舉世習行而不覺其非，可為痛哭流涕長太息者，七也！

法界佛教總會

美國「萬佛聖城」是西方佛教史上第一座大道場，它是宣化上人所成立的，乃西方佛教的發源地，所謂萬佛城，成萬佛，萬佛都來成。

而，萬佛聖城是「法界佛教總會」這把大傘蓋的總部。這把大傘，廣而言之是盡虛空、遍法界的；以我們這個世界來說，略而言之，就是所有宣化上人座下的道場、機構。

它
──以法界為體。
──以將佛教的真實義理，傳播到世界各地為目的。
──以翻譯經典、弘揚正法、提倡道德教育、利樂一切有情
　　為己任。

為此，上人立下家風：
凍死不攀緣，餓死不化緣，窮死不求緣，
隨緣不變，不變隨緣，
抱定我們三大宗旨：
捨命為佛事，造命為本事，正命為僧事。
即事明理，明理即事，推行祖師一脈心傳。

有人問：法界佛教總會自從一九五九年創立以來，它有多少道場？
　　　　──近 30 座，遍佈美、亞洲。
　　　　其中僧眾本著上人所創的「六大條款」：不爭、不貪、不求、不自私、不自
　　　　利、不妄語為依循；並恪遵佛制：日中一食、衣不離體。持戒念佛，習教
　　　　參禪，和合共住地獻身佛教。

又有人問：它有多少機構？
　　　　──國際譯經學院、法界宗教研究院、僧伽居士訓練班、法界佛教大學、培
　　　　德中學、育良小學等。

這傘蓋下的道場、機構，門戶開放，沒有人我、國籍、宗教的分別，凡是各國各教人
士，願致力於仁義道德、明心見性者，歡迎您前來修持，共同研習！

法界佛教總會及分支道場

法界佛教總會・萬佛聖城
Dharma Realm Buddhist Association &
The City of Ten Thousand Buddhas
P.O. Box 217
4951 Bodhi Way, Ukiah, CA 95482 U.S.A.
Tel: (707) 462-0939   Fax: (707) 462-0949
http://www.drba.org

國際譯經學院
The International Translation Institute
1777 Murchison Drive
Burlingame, CA 94010-4504 U.S.A.
Tel: (650) 692-5912   Fax: (650) 692-5056

法界宗教研究院（柏克萊寺）
Institute for World Religions
  (Berkeley Buddhist Monastery)
2304 McKinley Avenue, Berkeley, CA 94703 U.S.A.
Tel: (510) 848-3440   Fax: (510) 548-4551

金山聖寺　**Gold Mountain Monastery**
800 Sacramento Street
San Francisco, CA 94108 U.S.A.
Tel: (415) 421-6117   Fax: (415) 788-6001

金聖寺　**Gold Sage Monastery**
11455 Clayton Road, San Jose, CA 95127 U.S.A.
Tel: (408) 923-7243   Fax: (408) 923-1064

法界聖城　**City of the Dharma Realm**
1029 West Capitol Avenue
West Sacramento, CA 95691 U.S.A.
Tel: (916) 374-8268   Fax: (916) 374-8234

金輪聖寺　**Gold Wheel Monastery**
235 North Avenue 58
Los Angeles, CA 90042 U.S.A.
Tel: (323) 258-6668   Fax: (323) 258-3619

長堤聖寺　**Long Beach Monastery**
3361 East Ocean Boulevard
Long Beach, CA 90803 U.S.A.
Tel/Fax: (562) 438-8902

福祿壽聖寺
Blessings, Prosperity, and Longevity Monastery
4140 Long Beach Boulevard, Long Beach, CA 90807 USA
Tel/Fax: (562) 595-4966

華嚴聖寺　**Avatamsaka Monastery**
1009 Fourth Avenue S.W.
Calgary, AB T2P 0K8 Canada
Tel/Fax: (403) 234-0644

華嚴精舍　**Avatamsaka Vihara**
9601 Seven Locks Road, Bethesda
MD 20817-9997 U.S.A.
Tel: (301) 469-8300

金峰聖寺　**Gold Summit Monastery**
233 First Avenue, West, Seattle, WA 98119 U.S.A.
Tel: (206) 284-6690   Fax: (206) 284-6918

金佛聖寺　**Gold Buddha Monastery**
248 E. 11th Avenue
Vancouver, B.C. V5T 2C3 Canada
Tel: (604) 709-0248   Fax: (604) 684-3754